A Red Howell Fit

Jorga Riggenbach
and
Beth Smith Aycock

To Don,
Remembering ranch life.
Jorg Riggenbach
Beth Smith Aycock

RAGING BROOK PRESS
Tucson, Arizona
www.RagingBrookPress.com

 Published by Raging Brook Press, Tucson, Arizona. 520-250-8393. First Edition.

Library of Congress Control Number: 2007937190

ISBN 9780974507804

Dedication

To Red Howell, wherever he is, for being ol' Red.

Acknowledgments

We deeply appreciate the help of all who have added interest and substance to this book.

We are thankful for our families and friends for their support and input. Their enthusiastic response encouraged us to write this requiem to all the old ranchers, ropers and cowboys who have played a part in the history of the Southwest, and to their wives. Without them, this desert country would still be just mining shacks, tent houses saloons, bordellos and cow camps.

Our special thanks to our sons, Rick Smith and Martin Riggenbach for their advice and editing.

To Jim McConnell, a talented musician, who "heard" the book in the music of his new album, *Wild and Woolly*. He inspired Beth to write a few songs and Jim's marvelous music gave us all energy. Jim's CD is truly cowboy.

We owe thanks to Mary Bingham, Armando Carrillo, Pat Gossett, Scott Green, Barb Green, Bob Hall, Donna Hall, Donald Honnas, Jim McConnell, Tony O'Connor, Dave Omart, Robin Pinto, Opha Probasco, Martin Riggenbach, Ray Slane, Sally Slane, Rick Smith, Breck Smith, Ron Sotardi, Leroy Webb and Joel White for keeping us straight on the history of homesteading, railroads, automobiles, buildings, guns and ranch life.

Our Western heritage inspired us to write this book.

About the Authors

Beth Smith Aycock was born in New Mexico and raised on cattle ranches. She moved to Arizona in the 1930s, where she married her cowboy sweetheart. Beth continued to ranch until a few years ago.

In addition to A Red Howell Fit, she is the author of *Round Up A Whirlwind.*

Jorga Riggenbach was born in Idaho and raised in rural Colorado. After traveling for many years, she settled in Arizona where she fell in love with the history and people of the Southwest.

In addition to A Red Howell Fit, she is the author of *The Agua Caliente Chronicles, A History of the Tanque Verde Valley.*

Prologue

The old man was dying. This was the first time he'd ever been in a hospital bed. The family waited in a small room across the hall from his. In a larger waiting area down the hall, a handful of men sat with their Stetsons on their laps. Old faces, young faces, middle-aged faces, handsome and ugly, but all were sad faces tonight.

They were cowboys and ranchers. Tanned, weathered faces crowned by pale white foreheads and slicked-back hair told the story of men who were seldom seen without their hats on.

Folks walking down the hallway who glanced at the cowboys may have wondered if the men were holding a prayer vigil. If the passerby was local, the idea would be quickly dismissed. Cowboys of that era weren't big on public displays and when they communicated with God it was alone and out on the range.

Tonight they were here to bid Red adios and *vaya con dios*. Maybe their presence and strength would sustain him a little longer. Red was hard to give up. Most had known him a long time. They had worked with him, roped with him, ranched next to him, drank with him and laughed with him. He was a legend.

This was not a planned get-together. Not one of the men knew that any of the others would be here tonight, but each knew Red was dying and wanted to be with Red as long as he was on this earth.

As the men came in, they howdied and shook and then fell silent. Cowboy-like, it was not good to show emotions.

After a while, one said, "Well, they broke the mold when Ol' Red was born. When he's gone, they'll never find anyone to fill his boots."

"Yeah," said another, "Red sure had big boots, didn't he? Just like his hat, his voice, his heart – all big. Boy howdy, didn't he have a good time living?"

That set them off – each had Red Howell stories that they probably all knew, but they laughed at them anyway. They went on and on and their recollections brought Red back to them and gave them some measure of comfort.

It was nearing midnight when Red's son, Clay, came to the door. They knew Old Red was gone.

One by one, they filed by Clay, shaking his hand. Some embraced him while others patted him on the shoulder before walking down the hall and out the front door. No one spoke a word. The legend was gone.

chapter One

Me and Pancho

March 1901

"Red, if you leave, I'll shoot you!" The old man grabbed the long rifle from behind the wagon seat, pulled it to his shoulder and sighted down the barrel at his grandson.

"Why, you stubborn old cuss. I've been following you around like a slave, cleaning up after you. I must have apologized to everybody in this town. You know that grandma and the folks are worried sick about us. They're probably waiting for us at Horsehead crossing. We've been here a week and I'm plumb fed up with you. And now, you're going to shoot me? Grandpa, we have to go today.

"I don't want to go without you, but I will." Red looked the old man in the eye. "I don't want my folks to have to come back to see what's wrong and lose all that time."

"You make one move to go and I'll shoot you dead center," the old man said. "You can't make the trip on that green bronc you're riding. Besides that, you'd get yourself lost the first day out. You don't know the roads and you're a green kid with no sense at all."

"I'll ask you one more time, grandpa, and then I'm leaving. I know you wouldn't shoot me in the back."

"Like hell I wouldn't. I've killed men for less than leaving me stranded in a hick town. I wouldn't bat an eye if I had to shoot you. A grandson who would go off and desert his grandpa needs shooting. You think I'm impressed by your temper? What is it your dad calls it? A Red Howell fit?" He waved the rifle unsteadily to emphasize his point.

"Go on, you quitter. This is just what I'd expect from a know-it-all like you. I'm itching to shoot you in the back. I might as well. You'll starve to death anyhow before you catch up with the folks. I'll just save you some suffering."

The rifle shook slightly in the old man's hands but he continued to hold it on his grandson as the boy swung into the saddle and moved slowly down the street into the Western sun.

Red felt the hair on the back of his neck prickle as he rode steadily away from the threatening old man, knowing that any minute the bullet would blow him out of the saddle. The old man was a good shot, drunk or sober. Red knew he was fair pickings, as he rode down the dusty, main street into the afternoon sun. He dared not look back.

Red finally reached to the bottom of the hill and followed the road to the right. For the first time he looked back. He was out of sight of his grandpa. He let out the breath he'd been holding.

Red felt cold as the sweat evaporated from his skin. He took off his hat and wiped his brow on his shirt sleeve.

I bet that crazy old son-of-a-gun pulled the trigger and it didn't fire. I hope that's what happened so he won't be forever sorry he didn't shoot me, like he threatened.

I'm in a hell of a mess. I didn't really want to do this by myself, but I sure ain't going back. My bluff didn't work and I'm up a creek.

Five wagons had left from Kerrville more than three-weeks-ago to make the arduous 110-mile trip, the first leg of their journey, through the rich, rolling-hill country of West Texas. With their livestock, the families were moving to New Mexico Territory where there was ranch land for the taking.

The story they told themselves was that Texas was too crowded. In reality, it was about money. The could sell their land in Kerrville, make money and put it into more cattle. The land they'd homestead would be free and by their calculations, this would be a move that would benefit the whole family. The family had been moving Westward since 1828 – now in the year 1901, they were still looking for that illusive ranching Eden that would allow the family to prosper and grow.

When the Howell wagons arrived in Sonora, old man Howell ran into a couple of drinking buddies.

"Mathilda," he called to his wife, "I'm going with these two fellows for a quick drink."

The family waited a week for him to sober up, but finally they could afford to wait no longer. The old man's quick drink had turned into a bender.

"Red," his father pulled him aside, "I hate to put this on you, son, but we can't afford to stay here any longer and your grandpa has made it known that he isn't leaving until he's darned good and ready. I want you to stay here and look after him for a few days. As soon as he realizes that we've gone, I'm sure he'll come to his senses and you two can head out. We'll stop at Horsehead crossing and wait as long as we can for you."

"Alright, Pa," Red answered.

"I'm sorry son, but you've spent more time with him than your brothers and he's always seemed to take a shine to you."

"Don't worry, Pa, I'll do the best I can."

A week had passed since the rest of the family had gone ahead. Red had all but given up hope of his grandfather's return to sobriety.

Red had lots of time to think about it, but he couldn't figure out what had run the old man off the tracks. Grandfather, William Howell III, had been anxious to look at new country. He'd seen a lot of country in his day: From Mississippi to the Indian Territory, to Texas and now to New Mexico. Red thought about all the great tales his grandfather had told him. The old man had been a hell-raiser. He'd also always been a difficult person, but nobody understood this current, complete defection from the family. He was sullen and withdrawn and a raging thirst for booze was the only call he heeded.

The grizzled old man slept in his covered wagon under a live-oak tree at the top of the main street in Sonora, Texas. A pair of hobbled work horses grazed nearby and 15-year-old Red Howell sat on his heels with his back against the trunk of the tree. He watched with interest, as laborers across the street worked steadily on a structure that he'd been told would be a new mercantile store next year. Masons labored at a slow but steady pace as they prepared the cream-colored native limestone and meticulously set in, block after block. The main street presented a constantly changing drama as the young man kept a surreptitious eye on the garrulous old drunk he called "grandfather." Today the old man had been in the wagon most of the day, tipping a bottle of something that passed for whiskey.

Sonora's main street included several saloons and for the past week, old man Howell usually walked down the street to start his day of serious drinking. Red noticed that the downhill walk to the saloons seemed ironically appropriate to the situation. At the end of the day, the old drunk often required his grandson's help to make it back up the street to the wagon.

There's no use thinking about the past when I've got such a long ways to go. He spurred the three-year-old pony that he had only ridden a couple of weeks. He sighted the sun as he was taught to do and guessed it was about 3:00.

I'll ride until almost dark and then I'll find a little patch of grass for Pancho.

I'll have to teach Pancho a few things. I'd banked on changing horses every day – this bay pony hardly knows how to carry a guy. I sure made a good trade with that Mexican man. I traded a mare and colt that I'd mavericked in the Texas hill country for Pancho. I could've made good cow horse out of him on this trip if I'd gone with the cattle. But, he'll learn plenty when I catch up with them.

Red's mind raced and he fought the waves of dread and panic that threatened to engulf him.

All I have is a green horse, an old saddle, my rifle, and a new Sunday suit in a gunnysack tied behind my saddle. This morning I filled my chap pockets with jerky like I always do. I have the three silver dollars that pa gave me in case I had to bail grandpa out of a scrape. Any other time, $3.00 in my pocket would make me feel rich as Midas. I wonder if there'll be any place to buy some horse feed and a little bacon and bread. I have my old rifle and a handful of shells. I've got my gun for protection. I'm not hungry yet, but I will be. I might have to shoot a jack rabbit and eat it. Ranches and towns are probably few and far between out here in West Texas.

He hadn't seen a human being since he'd ridden out of town. He was thirsty, tired and knew his young horse needed a rest. It was March of 1901 and when the sun went down on the West Texas plains, it turned cold. Red shivered in his thin jacket.

Just as the sun dropped below the horizon, he saw a set of corrals and a little homesteader's house huddled beneath a wind mill.

He rode on up to the front of the house and yelled, "Hello the house," as he'd heard his folks do. A big, Texas-looking man opened the patched screen door, peered through the lessening light at Red and said, "What do you want young man? Where are you headin'? What's your name?"

Red stuttered a bit – he finally got sounds out of his dry throat and said, "Mister, I'm Red Howell from Kerrville. I'm trying to catch up with my family who passed by here last week going to New Mexico Territory. I just wondered if I could get a drink there at your windmill and water my horse. We're awful dry."

The rancher sized Red up. "Go ahead and water your horse. Get a drink and come back to the porch. I want to look you over."

Pancho slurped from the trough as Red leaned over and drank gratefully from the pipe.

Boy, this water tastes good.

When neither the boy nor the horse could hold another drop of water, Red tied Pancho to a post and headed back to the front porch. He stood waiting for the man to speak.

"My name is Ephriam Kenny."

Red stepped to the porch and said, "I'm pleased to meet you, Mr. Kenny."

"How old are you, son?" Kenny asked.

"I'll be sixteen in July, sir. I'm about grown."

"So," Kenny said, "you're 15 and you're crossing West Texas on young horse. Did you kill somebody? Are you trying to beat the law to the border?"

"No, sir." Red was getting nervous. He realized it did look strange for a kid to be in the fix he was in. "My grandpa was supposed to be with me, but he couldn't make it, so I'm trying to catch up with my folks." Red was careful not to tell Mr. Kenny the real reason grandpa couldn't make it.

"Son, put your horse in the corral and feed him some corn out of the bin in the barn nearest the corral. I'll fix us something to eat. Where is your bed roll?"

Again, Red was at a loss to answer.

"Guess that gunny sack on your saddle has a blanket, huh?"

Red replied in a low and halting voice. "No sir, that's my Sunday suit. I don't have a bed roll."

"That's a hell of a way to travel," Kenny said.

"Yes, sir, I had to leave in a hurry."

"You're not telling me everything, young man," Kenny said. "I've heard about the Howells. They had a lot of cattle on Devil's River. Kinda hooked up somehow with the Lackeys and Zumwalts, huh?"

"Yes, sir, that's our family." Red didn't like being pumped for information, but it was dusk and he was hungry and lonesome.

"Old man Howell was mean rascal. Killed a man, didn't he? Guess you had to shoot him to get away, huh?"

"No sir, I never shot nobody. My grandpa was going to shoot me if I left him. I don't know why he didn't, but I ain't going back."

"Go on, feed your horse. You can sleep here tonight."

Mr. Kenny fried some steak and made some gravy and biscuits. Red didn't disappoint him. He ate his share. Red was more content than he had been all day.

By the time he left the next morning, Red had learned a great deal about Mr. Kenny: He had some cattle. His wife had died last year. He was from up around the settlement. He'd been here for five years. And, Red realized, Kenny was lonesome for company.

Red hated to leave. He told Mr. Kenny how grateful he was for a place to spend his first night. He thanked him for the advice about the folks he could trust and the ones he should avoid. Kenny suggested a few little towns where Red could stay on the wagon road.

"Red, you can buy some victuals and horse feed as you travel. It's better to stay on the main trail than to cut across country to save a few miles. You never know when your horse will play out. If that happened, you'd be up a creek."

Mr. Kenny tied another gunny sack to Red's saddle horn.

"Son, this isn't much, just the cold biscuits left from breakfast and a good sized piece of bacon, plus some horse feed."

Red tried to pay him, but Mr. Kenny refused. As he watched Red ride off that morning, his heart ached.

If my boy had lived, he'd be about that age. I'd sure have liked for him to have had the guts that redheaded scoundrel has. I like that kid. I wish I had somebody like that to take over the ranch when I die.

"Oh, well," he said aloud. "That's just the cards I was dealt. I better saddle up and ride that other pasture."

Chapter Two

Aw, Pancho, Why?

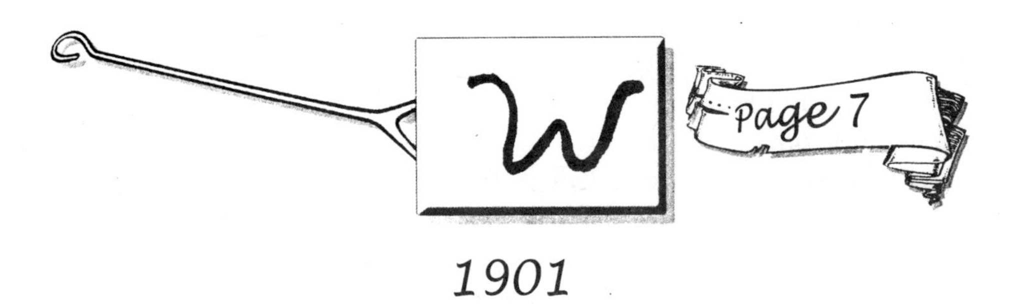

1901

Red figured he made about 20 miles the second day. He couldn't crowd Pancho or he'd be afoot on these miserable plains without feed or water. The west wind he was riding into blew incessantly, stirring up an occasional whirlwind. The red, Texas dust never let up. By nightfall his face was blistered and grimy. Tonight he'd have to make a dry camp.

In a little coulee, Red found some protection from the wind. He hoped it would let up at sundown. Pancho, unsaddled and hobbled, grazed on last year's grass.

Red was dead tired. He built a small, mesquite fire. He cut off a couple of strips of bacon and had a fine supper with one cold biscuit and a slice of the onion Mr. Kenny had packed for him.

By the time he had checked Pancho and gotten ready to bed down, a cold wind blew from north. Red built up the fire, unpacked his new serge suit from the back of his saddle and put the vest, coat and trousers on over his work clothes.

He spread the gunny sack and saddle blanket out, curled up with his saddle for a pillow and went to sleep immediately. You can't cheat youth.

He was awakened a few times during the night by the howl of a coyote. Red briefly wondered if the coyote was as lonesome as he was. Red threw a little more brush on the fire. Pancho was standing hip-shot, probably sleeping too. Red lay back down on his pallet. This time he crawled under the damp saddle blanket because the temperature had dropped. He slept like a log until dawn.

After a lean breakfast, he brushed off Pancho's back with the saddle blanket and shook out the dirt. He put the blanket on Pancho, threw on the saddle, tightened the cinch and felt Pancho hump up.

It feels like Pancho has a cold back this morning.

Red shook out his good Sunday suit, now covered with gunny sack fuzz and a few other unnecessary adornments, smoothed it out, rolled it up and packed it.

I'm sure glad I brought it. Without that old suit, I'd a froze to death last night. Ma'll scold about it, but she'll clean it up good as new when I get to Seven Rivers.

Everything packed and in place, Red stepped on Pancho without leading him around a bit to uncork him. Before he could catch his off stirrup, Pancho broke in two with him and Red went sailing off. When Red hit the ground he was still holding one rein, otherwise Pancho would have been back in Kerrville in a day and Red left afoot in the middle nowhere.

Holding Pancho with a short rein, Red kicked him in the belly a couple of times and called him a few uncomplimentary names. Red stepped on quickly, whirled Pancho around in a short circle, got the kinks out of his back and rode off.

Chapter Three

Horsehead Crossing

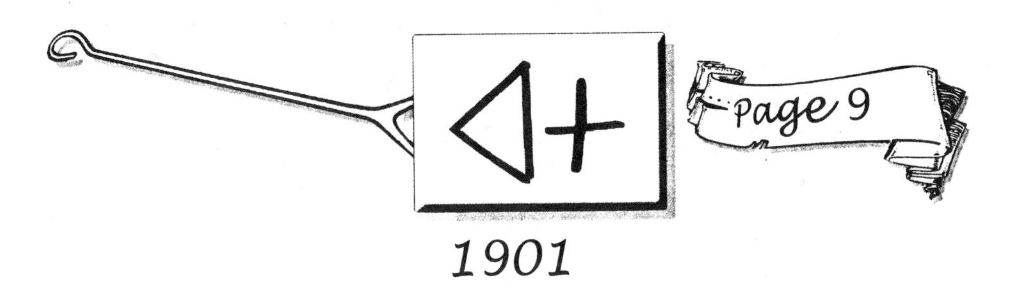

1901

The five wagons were pulled up into a semicircle beside the muddy Pecos River at Horsehead Crossing awaiting the arrival of the sixth wagon. There was no longer an Indian threat, but it was still practical and customary to camp this way. The arrangement corralled the children and the centrally located campfire meant fewer steps for the women.

The Howell men unharnessed the work horses. A night guard was appointed to keep an eye on things and loose herd the cattle and horses. The women quickly built a cook-fire. The wagons broke the incessant west wind a tad. The younger children played within the semicircle of wagons while the older children completed their assigned chores.

There were plenty of children. Uncle Billy Howell and his wife, Sarah, had six: Red, Jim, Dovie, Ruth, Tom and Levi. Landis and Elsie, not to be outdone, also had six. To make matters more complicated, they were, as the Texans called them, first-double-cousins. Billy and Landis were brothers and Sarah and Elsie were sisters.

When they were on the trail, the women and older boys drove the wagons most of the time. Occasionally, when the men were in a mellow mood, they swapped off and let the women drive the herd while they took over the lowly task of driving the heavily loaded wagons.

"Riding herd on the youngsters," Landis remarked, "is a hell of a lot harder than keeping the cows pointed the right direction." The other men nodded in fervent agreement.

Grandma Mathilda Howell, whose husband was currently on the

unscheduled bender in Sonora, drove her own wagon. There was usually a grandchild or two on the seat keeping her company.

She told wonderful stories that seemed to make the slow travel pass in a flash. To the children, she was very exotic. Imagine, a grandmother who was half Cherokee Indian. She often spoke of a trip — she called it the *Trail of Tears* — that she'd been forced to endure. The youngsters felt grown-up when she explained that Grandpa Howell had been disowned from his family for marrying her.

"Grandma, what was it like? Was it scary to live with all those Indians?"

"Son, I lived with Indians all my life, just like you have lived with your folks in Texas."

"Why did they make you go away from your home? Did they make us leave our place in Texas?"

"Well, you don't have to worry. The problem for us was that the white folks kept wanting to take our land and the government backed them up. First, they forced us out of the Carolinas and made us go to Florida. The people sickened in that swampy country down there and many died. Soon, they even wanted that place, so they said they'd set some land aside for us in the Oklahoma Territory. Many of the people were tired and didn't want to go, but they forced everyone to leave Florida. So, many people died and we shed many tears on that trail."

"Were the Indians mean, grandma? Is that why they kept making them move?"

"No, son, but if you want to talk about mean, your grandpa was a whole lot meaner than any Indian I ever knew." She smiled to let him know that she wasn't entirely serious.

"Your grandpa," she continued, "always managed to pick a fight. I think it must have had something to do with the way he was raised down there in Mississippi. I met him while I was on the march and we married. I have to give him credit. He went with me on up to Oklahoma and we made our own family.

"Lord have mercy, that was good cow country. The herd of cows and horses that William brought with us was sizeable. In fact, it was downright miraculous. Why, son, those cows of grandpa's all seemed to be having twins. Not only that, but the neighbors' cows turned up with full udders and no calves."

"Then what happened, grandma?"

"Well, it didn't look too good to the neighbors and at some point, the decision was made to excuse us from the Cherokee Nation. They gave grandpa a new name as a good-bye present. They called him, *nzaagyu tlool*. That means something like, 'Man with a long rope.' From there, we moved on over to Texas."

"I guess that's where you learned to drive so good, grandma. You sure can handle these work horses."

"I've had a lot of practice, Will. How about you getting in some practice yourself?" She handed him the reins. "You drive awhile."

Taking a break from driving, Mathilda wondered when her husband would catch up to the wagons. She wasn't too worried about him, but she was uneasy about Red.

The fourth day at Horsehead Crossing was the breakaway day. They paid Mr. MacKay for the well water they'd used. They also paid him to help push the cattle across the river, which was no easy job. Next came the heavily loaded wagons. The Pecos was running deep and swift from the spring snow melt in Northern New Mexico

Mr. MacKay drove Grandma Howell's wagon across. The team, fed and rested, was raring to go.

The wagons made it across. Not one calf drowned and none of the livestock was washed down the stream. The price was high – Mr. MacKay did nothing for free. The Howells didn't mind. It was a dangerous crossing and they were happy to have his expertise and knowledge of the Pecos.

They were all glad to be on the move again. They were looking forward to the time when they could to get out of the wagons into a house.

The women had the worst end of the deal – cooking over a campfire, trying to keep them all clean. No one was starched and ironed.

Sarah looked back across the Pecos, hoping at the last-minute to see Mr. Howell and her son, Red.

The wagon road they were on now was more heavily traveled than the one across West Texas. It was the main route between Pecos, Texas and Eddy, New Mexico Territory.

They would hit the settlement of Seven Rivers, their destination, in a few days. The relatives – more Howells from Texas – had preceded them. All had staked their claims, built houses and started their ranches on the open land.

Will, Pa and me

Chapter Four

Trying to Catch Up

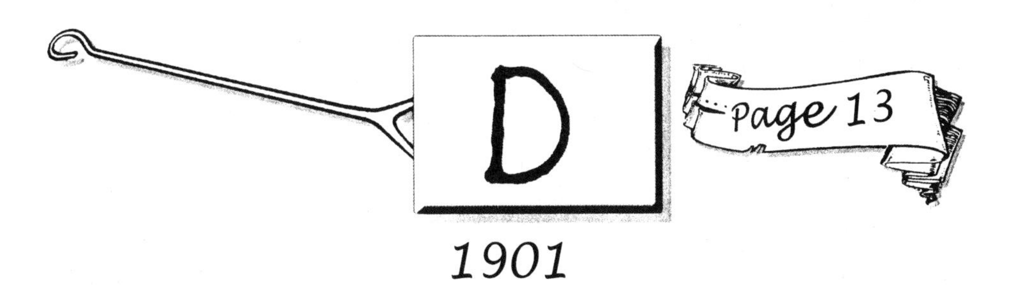

1901

Day after day the west wind pounded Red. He often doubted that he was on the right road. Sometimes the way was so faintly marked that he wondered if he was even on a road. He pondered on the fact that all the Texans heading West seemed to take a different route.

Some days he followed deep wagon ruts. Other times he followed a trail that the last folks he had encountered recommended as a short cut. Many times he made a dry camp because the river or windmill someone had described was not where it was supposed to be. He and Pancho were always thirsty.

They were hungry, too. Red was down to five bullets for his old 30-30. It was hard to hit a cottontail with a 30-30. It blew most of the edible meat to Kingdom Come. Jack rabbits were larger and it was possible to get a head shot.

"You know, Pancho, I've had to eat a few jack rabbits on this trip. I would almost rather go hungry. Our chuck sure is slim."

Red had gotten in the habit of talking out loud to Pancho.

"I reckon if I didn't talk to you, Pancho, my voice would just dry up. I ain't been having many conversations with folks these days."

Occasionally, he'd strike a ranch around the end of the day and most of the time he was invited to eat with the family or at the bunkhouse kitchen. He knew it wasn't polite to have second and third helpings. It sure was tough being well mannered.

As he passed by the few, small towns in West Texas, he used his carefully hoarded cash for horse feed, bacon and bread. Once, he couldn't overcome the pressing hunger for a nickel's worth of candy.

Later, he told Pancho about it. "Boy, did it taste good. I promise you that when I'm grown up and have my own ranch, I'll always have a dish of candy out for the kids and the cowboys." Pancho flicked his ears back and forth in approval.

Once or twice, Red was fortunate to get a few days work at a ranch or dry land farm. He worked for his board and horse feed. Pancho needed a few days off. The colt was just a coming three-year-old. He was still limber and this trip had forced him onto a slim diet.

Red figured he was making 20 miles-a-day. He'd stop and get directions at the little towns that had a post office in a small store. The mail was delivered once a week from San Antonio. These little hardscrabble towns had a few houses and the residents made a living any way they could. For the life of him, Red couldn't figure out why people lived in these places. They certainly weren't here for the scenery.

The landscape changed subtly. He passed miles and miles of low, rocky hills with a little brush on them. Sandy draws that only ran in the rainy season bisected the dry earth. The grass was brown and patchy. It was desolate looking country.

Day by day he progressed.

"Excuse me, sir, how far it to Horsehead Crossing on the Pecos River?" Red always asked the same question when he encountered a fellow traveler or someone in a town.

"You know, Pancho, it seems like it's a million miles to Horsehead Crossing."

His booger reds, the brand-name of cheap work clothes he wore, were getting threadbare. At one of the farms where he'd worked, the good lady of the house made up a package for him. It contained a little food, a pair of socks and a bar of homemade lye soap. He treasured the gift.

When he was traveling near a running creek or river if the weather was warm enough, he'd try to clean up. He'd leave his ten-gallon hat on the bank with his worn-out, run-over boots. Once in the water, Red scrubbed his clothes with a little sand and lye soap. He draped the wet clothes on the bushes to dry while he scrubbed himself. Out of the water, he put on his serge suit without a shirt and hoped his clothes would dry by bedtime.

"You know, Pancho, I must be a sight to behold. Here I am, fifteen-years-old in the middle of nowhere. Ma always tells folks that I'm redheaded as a woodpecker. She says my freckles go with my red hair."

Red rubbed his jaw, considering how to describe himself. When he took his hand away, he announced, "I believe there's little fuzz starting there." Red looked at his huge hands. He raised them to his hair.

"Damn, my hair is growing down over my ears. I hate that. Ma always kept our hair cut short." Red's unfolded his six-foot frame and checked his drying clothes.

"I guess the long hair doesn't matter, Pancho. After all, I'm not running for governor, standing a stud horse or trying to get married. I'm just headed for Horsehead Crossing."

The closer he came to crossing the Pecos, the more he crowded Pancho.

He stopped for the night near a ranch that seemed less desolate than the ones he had been seeing. There was a fence around a carefully tended yard. In the center stood a prim, white-painted, little cottage with real curtains on the clean windows. A couple of hound dogs barked without enthusiasm as he rode up.

Red was so lonesome for his ma that he just sat there on his rode-down horse and let the tears run down his sun-and-wind blistered face.

A lady wearing a long, full-skirted gingham dress under a snow-white apron with big patch pockets greeted him from the porch.

"Howdy son, where you headed?" She asked.

"Ma'am, I'm on my way to Seven Rivers settlement in New Mexico Territory, but I'm hoping to catch up with my ma and pa's outfit at Horsehead Crossing. Do you know how much farther it is?"

The lady looked him over closely. He was sort of pitiful looking and younger than he appeared when she first saw him. If she noticed the tear streaks on his freckled face, she didn't mention it.

"You are only a few miles from the crossing, young man. I don't believe there is anyone there waiting to cross from this side. My man helped a family named Howell cross several weeks ago. They went over with their cattle and horses, but they're long gone."

Red's face fell. "I'm a Howell, ma'am," he said. "Name's Red. I got delayed back in Sonora and have tried hard to catch up but I guess I'm too late."

"They stayed down by the crossing for a few days waiting for someone who never showed up – guess they were waiting for you. Where's the rest that were supposed to be with you? Did they turn back?"

"No ma'am," Red answered. "I just come on by myself. My grandpa didn't want to come and I knew my folks would worry about us."

"You poor child, all that way by yourself. It must have been horrible," the lady said.

"Yes, ma'am, I got scared a time or two, but I couldn't turn back. I'll go on down to the river and camp. 'Fraid it's too late to try to get across tonight," Red said, as he turned his horse to go.

"Son, you better stay here tonight and my man will help you cross in the morning. That ol' river is mighty treacherous. That's why we are here and that's how we make our living: Helping folks across for pay."

"But Ma'am, I couldn't pay very much. I had three silver dollars when my folks left me to bring grandpa. My horse threw a fit and threw me off a way back there and I lost one of my dollars. The other two has bought me a little food, some oats for my horse, and I've just got a two-bit piece left. I know that's not enough." He sighed.

"You go water your horse and put him in that far corral. Wash yourself at the water trough in the pen where you put your horse and come back and eat supper," she ordered.

"No, ma'am I can't do that," Red said.

"I don't know why in the world you can't. What's wrong with you, boy?"

"Well, ma'am, I don't have any money to pay you, like I said, and I don't need charity."

"Come on, son, we might charge for well water and our help to cross the Pecos, but we ain't heathens. We like to help folks that need it. I'm not saying you couldn't make it without us, but I'm partial to boys. I had five myself and I miss them. They all grew up and now they work for ranches and cattle drives. It'll tickle my man, too, to have you here," she said.

Red rode off slowly thinking of what to do. At the corral he unsaddled Pancho, rubbed him down, watered and fed him.

"Now," he said to Pancho, "I've got to slick up. I know I can't help myself much, but I'll give it a try."

He stripped off the worn shirt, got out his soap – careful not to get any soap in the horse trough – and scrubbed his mop of red, curly hair. He slicked it down with his fingers. His pulled his old shirt back on. He took off his chaps and hung them on his saddle. With a gunnysack, he dusted his boots off.

Damn, I'm so hungry I could eat a polecat.

Chapter Five

The Big Break

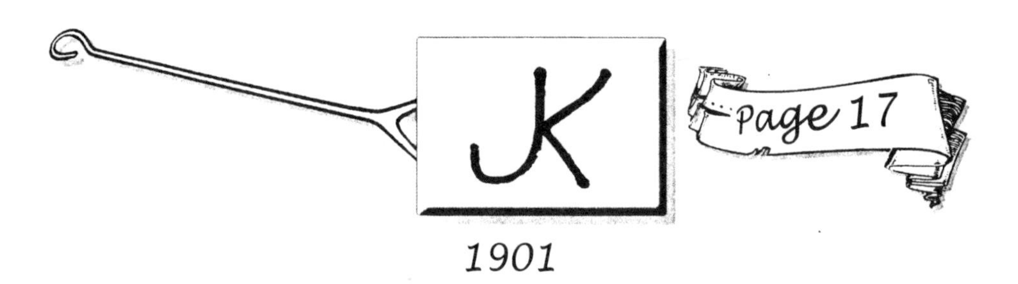

1901

While Red was trying to make himself presentable to Mrs. MacKay, her husband, Dan, rode in. He was a kindly looking man, weathered and older than his wife, Red thought.

Red walked over and opened the corral gate for him and took the reins as the man got off his sweaty horse. You could tell he'd put in a day.

"Howdy, I'm Red Howell. The missis said I could stay the night and you'd help me cross in the morning. I'll tend to your horse, sir, if you'll tell me how you want it done."

Dan MacKay was impressed.

Stopping for a minute, Mr. MacKay held out his hand and shook Red's, noting that the boy's hand, big as a dinner plate, was freckled and sunburned.

"I'm Dan MacKay. Glad to make your acquaintance, son. I believe your folks were just here for a few days. Nice folks. It must have been you they were waiting on."

"Yes, sir," Red answered, "they were waiting for me and my grandpa. I'd have gotten here quicker, but things didn't work out too good."

Red and Dan worked together in amiable silence, as they unsaddled Dan's horse, rubbed him down and turned him out into the corral. Red forked some hay into the wooden trough while Dan took the saddle, bridle and blanket into the shed. Dan took a few moments to wash a couple layers of grime off his hands and face.

"Let's see what the old lady has cooked up for us. Bet you could eat just about anything. You're looking gutted," Dan observed as they headed up to the house.

"Yes, sir, I've kinda been on short rations and it has been a far piece between water holes."

"Didn't you have a canteen, son?"

"No, sir, I left Sonora without much of anything."

"I heard about your grandpa getting drunk," Dan spoke softly.

"Well, sir, it probably wasn't the thing for me to do, but I couldn't get him to sober up and he sure wasn't planning to move on any time soon, so I left without him. He wasn't pleased with my decision and let me know by threatening to shoot me."

"You sure took a chance coming on by yourself, but you made it and I don't blame you a bit for leaving the old man behind."

The supper was the best Red had eaten since he left home in Kerrville. Just before the family hit the road, ma cooked a Farewell-to-Texas dinner and invited all the neighbors.

Now, he was tucking into fried chicken, biscuits and gravy, frijole beans and he saw an apple pie for dessert. The pie, made from dried apples, scented the house with a smell so heady and sweet that Red felt like he might die with pleasure.

He tried to eat as politely as his ma had taught him but the MacKays urged him to have another helping and he obliged them. Boy, was it good.

After supper, Mrs. MacKay led him to the spare room. Red stopped in the doorway and stared in amazement. White, ruffled curtains covered the windows. A starched, ironed, white sheet covered the bed and the bureau sported a delicately embroidered dresser scarf.

Red backed up, "No Ma'am," he stuttered, "I ain't gonna mess up this pretty room. I sure thank you, but it just ain't right. If you trust me with your horses, I'd sure rather sleep in the barn and I wouldn't feel so obligated to you folks. I don't want to make more work for you."

Mrs. MacKay could see by the stubborn set of his jaw, that she wasn't going to prevail.

"Alright, boy," she said, "we'll get you settled in the barn."

Red sighed with relief. "I'll help you clean up the kitchen. I always helped my ma and grandma. Don't worry. I won't break anything."

Mrs. MacKay laughed and gave Red a hug as they walked companionably to the kitchen. It sure felt good to Red – like being home.

Red spent a comfortable night in a hay loft. For the first time in days he felt safe when he fell asleep. He didn't have to worry about his horse getting boogered or any surprises in the night. He'd been sleeping with one eye open for days. He awoke feeling relaxed and refreshed for the first time in long while.

The next morning he sat down to a breakfast of ham, eggs, biscuits and honey. As they finished up, Mr. MacKay said, "Red, I was looking at your horse this morning. He's pretty gimpy. Why don't you stay here a few days and let your horse get on his feet again so you can make it to Seven Rivers. You have another hundred miles to go and I could use some help."

Red looked him straight in the eye and said, "Thank you, Mr. MacKay. It would sure make me feel better to pay you all back with some work."

Mr. MacKay grinned. "Well, Red, I've got an even better deal. I'll pay you. I've got some big calves that need branding before screwworm time. I've been thinking that some of my boys would come home and help me. I had a good man working for me, but I made the mistake of paying him his wages the other day and he took off. I guess he's on a toot down at Pecos. It's like the cowboys say, 'It's payday and Saturday night and I gotta go to town to town and get drunk and Lord, how I dread it.'"

This tickled Red and for the first time in a long while, he had a good belly laugh.

My sister Ruth

These ladies gave me this picture at one of the ranches I stopped at so I'd remember them. I remember them but I forgot their names right away.

Chapter Six

Cowboying on the Pecos

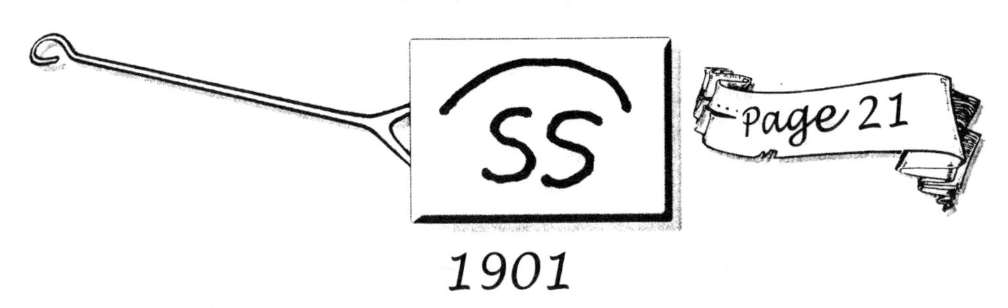

1901

"Yes, sir, I'd sure like to help you work cattle, but I don't want no pay. I still owe you for last night and those two good meals."

They pushed away from the breakfast table and headed for the corral.

"I don't have a big country," MacKay said, "but it's hard to work. "Most of the cows run down in the salt cedars by the Pecos. It's good shelter from the wind and they eat the salt grass that grows there. It's only good when it sprouts out in the spring. I like to brand when the cows are doing good on that salt grass and before screw-worm time."

"Catch that big, bay horse with the streak-face. When you're on him, you'll know you're mounted. I'll ride the big sorrel."

Red quickly and efficiently caught the bay, brushed him off, and saddled him. He also made sure his lariat was on the ready. Texas cowboys tied hard and fast, just in case the occasion arose to rope something.

They gathered quite a good bunch of cows, some with big calves and some with younger ones. They drove them back to the corrals at the ranch. Mrs. MacKay had a big, hot meal ready for them and the man and boy fell into it like they hadn't eaten for a week.

After lunch, Mr. MacKay and Red went to the corrals and resaddled their horses. As they began to cut the calves off from their mothers, the dust churned and the din of bawling calves and mamas frantically calling their babies filled the air. The men worked with steady determination, moving the separated calves off to another pen.

When the cows and calves were separated and the noise diminished a notch or two, Red gathered wood for the branding fire and MacKay got the irons, piggin' strings, and some creosote and grease to use as an ointment so the fresh brands would peel off and heal faster.

They worked well together. Dan was a good roper and Red a good flanker. Red got the calves down and tied without much to-do about it. He had been well taught by his pa and both grandfathers in the art of flanking and tying down a calf.

After about the fifteenth calf, Dan MacKay said, "Red, you want to rope awhile? I didn't gather my slack fast enough and that last calf sure put a rope burn on my hand. I'd like to let it cool off while you take my place. You can rope, can't you?"

"Yes, Sir, I've roped a few, but I'm not as good as you are, that's for sure. I don't want you down here in the dirt flanking these calves, sir."

"I'm not as worn-out as you seem to think I am, Red. I left all the little calves for a reason. I want to see what you can do."

Red tightened his cinch and uncoiled his rope. It was a sorry rope – beat-up and dirty from staking Pancho night after night.

"Mr. MacKay, do you want them headed or heeled?"

"Anyway you can catch 'em, boy."

Red rode quietly into the herd, picked out a small, unbranded calf, slapped his loop on him and dragged the calf to the branding fire. Mr. MacKay flanked the calf and hog-tied him neatly. Red was impressed. He thought Dan MacKay, who was probably in his 50s, should be sitting in a rocking chair on the front porch swatting flies.

They worked hard, joshed each other when one missed a loop or when a calf Dan had tied managed to struggle back to its feet.

It sure is good, Red thought, *to be treated like a man instead of a snot-nosed kid.*

When the cows and calves had all mothered up, they turned out to the pasture. Dan and Red washed in the horse trough and headed up to the house.

Dan glanced at the gangly, fifteen-year-old and shook his head. *Someday soon, this young man is going to be a top roper*, he thought.

The evening was unusually warm for March. They sat on the front porch eating molasses cookies and drinking buttermilk.

They related the events of the day to Mrs. MacKay. Their droll recounting of the day's events delighted Cora and she used her apron to cover her mouth as she laughed with them.

After a companionable lull in the conversation, Dan said, "Red, how'd you like to stay here and work for us? You're a good hand and I need somebody to help me. Working the cattle and the Crossing keeps me busier than a bee. And mama here needs another cowboy to cook for. She's been happier the past couple of days than she's been for a while. I'm afraid she'll turn cranky on me when you hit the trail."

The MacKays both laughed, but Red didn't. He knew he had to make a decision.

"Mr. MacKay, more than anything in the world, I'd like to stay here with you all. The thing is, ma and pa don't know where I am. I have to go up to Seven Rivers and let 'em know about grandpa and me. They'll worry themselves sick if I don't get on up there."

"I knew you'd say that, Red. You're not the sort who'd let his parents down like that. The thing is, we could send a letter up to your kin with some of the folks who are crossing. You can write, can't you Red?"

"Yes, sir, I graduated tenth grade. I can write, do figures and I studied history, geography and some algebra. I was going on to the upper grades when my folks decided to move to New Mexico. I sure did hate to quit school like that. Maybe I can go on in New Mexico, but I doubt it because I've heard that country up there is raw."

"Well, Red, I'd appreciate it if you'd give it some thought tonight. We can talk about it in the morning. Now it's time to get the chores done and get ready for supper. You better give that rode-down horse of yours an extra ration of grain tonight. That way, if you decide to hit the trail, he'll have some bottom to him."

After supper, Red sat by himself with his head in his hands. *Why do I have to make all these decisions by myself? I'd like to earn some money and let Pancho rest. Mr. MacKay would pay me a fair wage and Mrs. MacKay sure is nice. If I got word to the folks, they probably wouldn't mind too much. What the hell, I'm nearly 16-years-old; it's time I started standing up on my own two legs.*

Bright and early the next morning, Dan said grace and they tucked into a hearty breakfast. "Red, I reckon I'll be needing to help you across the river today. I'll lead Pancho and you can ride one of my horses across – that way Pancho won't have to pack so much weight. I don't know how high the river is this morning. Are you all packed?"

Red laughed. "It don't take much time to pack my gear."

"I thought about your offer a whole lot last night and if someone comes by who you think is reliable and headed the right direction, I'll ask them to deliver or mail a letter to my folks. I'd like to stay here and help you awhile and I'd sure like to sample some more of Mrs. Burns cooking."

Grandpa and Grandma Lackey

Chapter Seven

Goodbyes Ain't No Fun

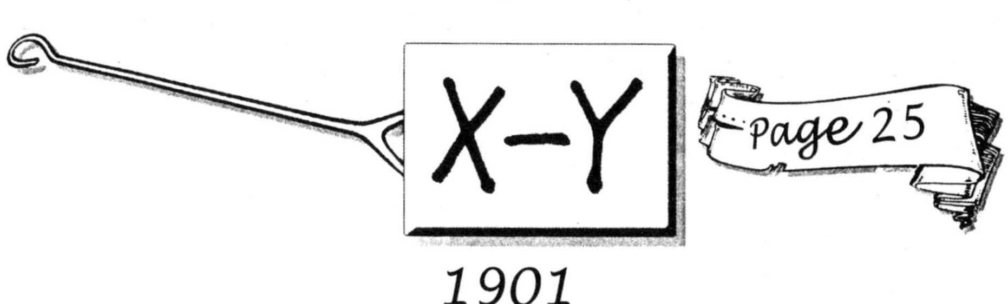

1901

As luck would have it, two wagons leaving Texas came by that morning. They were headed for the Block Ranch. Red knew the Block brand. John S. Chisum owned it and his Grandpa Lackey had been Chisum's trail boss at one time.

As a child, Red spent many an evening listening to Grandpa Lackey tell about punching cows on the Chisum Ranch and about the Lincoln County Wars. Red knew grandpa's story of the ranch by heart: The ranch was the biggest spread in New Mexico Territory. Chisum's ranch was as big as some countries in the Old World. It was bigger than the state of Rhode Island. Why, boy, from north to south it was 150 miles and 100 miles from east to west. They ran 80,000 head of cattle.

Red's favorite stories were about Billy the Kid. Grandpa said it was during this time that the family got to know him. They claimed he taught Red's ma, Sarah, to shoot a pistol when she was seven-years-old.

"Every so often," grandpa said, "Billy came by, ate supper with us, and spent the night. Once, in passing conversation, I told him how I recently came up short 18 cows. After supper, without saying a word, Billy left the table and rode off. Three days later he came back with all 18 cows."

I asked grandma once if Billy had to kill somebody to get those cows back. She looked at me sternly and said, "You don't ask."

Red borrowed a sheet of paper from Mrs. MacKay and laboriously penned a note to his folks explaining the situation. It was difficult to tell about leaving Grandpa Howell in Sonora.

I reckon I should have written to them sooner.

He explained his situation and said that they could get in touch with him by sending a letter to the MacKays. He addressed the letter: To Any Howell in the Vicinity of Seven Rivers, New Mexico Territory. He knew that anyone who received it would get word to his ma and pa.

Red stayed at the MacKay's Ranch until the work was all done that fall. He received letters from his folks quite often. His pa had bought some land near a small town called Hope. They were building a house in the section nearest town so his younger brothers and his sister could attend school.

Late that fall, Red told Mr. MacKay that he wanted to go on to New Mexico. He had learned a great deal during the months he had worked with Dan MacKay.

He enjoyed the cowboying most of all and he had become increasingly proficient at his tasks. He made a good hand and he kept his temper, even with some of the foolish people who made the river crossing.

During the summer, he met people from many states and enjoyed all the tales they had to tell about their travels and adventures. Sometimes he felt a longing to see new places and explore new country, but hard work from dawn until dusk quieted the call of the road. He made himself content to stay and earn his first, real money.

Mr. MacKay was paying him $15 a month and board. This was a gold mine for Red. He hadn't drawn any wages and the day he left he had accumulated the unbelievable sum of $90. Even though it worried him, he was pleasantly surprised when Mr. MacKay wouldn't subtract the cost of the work clothes, hat and boots Red had sent for. MacKay said it was his bonus.

Red's improved wardrobe boasted a new, high-crowned, black Stetson and a pair of high-topped, off-the-shelf boots that he kept for Sundays. Mr. MacKay had a set of shoe lasts and he resoled Red's work boots.

Cora MacKay had delighted in making Red three work shirts and

Red also bought a couple of pairs of Levi Strauss denim jeans to replace the old patch-upon-patch Booger-Reds he'd worn when he left Kerrville.

Red choked up when he told Mrs. MacKay goodbye. With the edge of her apron, she brushed the tears from her eyes and hugged him fiercely. They had grown so close. Only his mother held a place in his heart that was as great as what he felt for Mrs. MacKay.

Crossing the Pecos this time of year was relatively easy. The spots with quicksand were well known and the current in the low water was sluggish.

On the north side of the river, the men dismounted. Shoulder to shoulder, they surveyed the MacKay spread on the other side of the river.

Red watched his foot as he scuffled the toe of his book in the sandy soil. Without looking up, he said, "Gosh, Mr. MacKay, I hope your new man works out for you. I sure don't relish the thought of leaving. You treated me good and I learned so much from you. I admire you. I won't forget you or the missis. If I ever get the chance, I'll be back on your doorstep."

MacKay turned and put out his hand. Red extended his big, freckled paw and they shook. MacKay mounted his horse and, without a backward glance, headed back across the Pecos.

"Well, Pancho, it looks like it's just the two of us again." Red spoke gently to the horse as he pulled himself into the saddle. He watched until MacKay had made it safely across the river and then he turned Pancho and headed up the road.

I don't know the way exactly, but I certainly feel better about this than I felt that day in March when I turned my back on grandpa and head.

One of Pa's colts

Chapter Eight

Home, Sweet Home

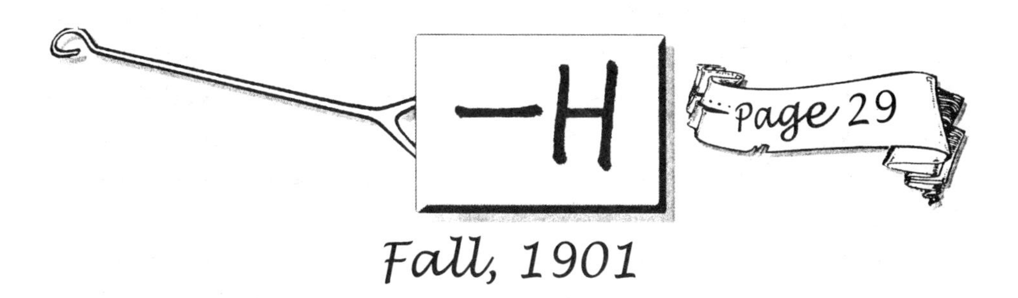

Fall, 1901

Red rode north. He saw a lot of flat country, but kept getting nearer and nearer to the Guadalupe Mountain range of southern New Mexico.

After West Texas, this was a Mecca – plenty of feed and water for Pancho and little settlements and ranches along the river where he could buy a few groceries.

Mrs. MacKay had given him more than he wanted to pack on Pancho, but he wouldn't have hurt her feelings by refusing her for anything in the world. He just rode a little slower and walked and led Pancho when they hit a few hills.

He was so anxious to see his family. It had been more than eight months since he saw their dust leaving Sonora. He was part of a close family, almost clannish. He knew they had moved from Seven Rivers to a town called Hope.

I don't know where Hope is but I've ridden across West Texas by myself. I've drawn wages for punching cows and I know I can do anything that needs to be done. I sure as hell can find Hope.

At Seven Rivers, he stayed with his Aunt Elsie and Uncle Landy. He was pleased to see his cousin, Will Howell, again. They had tales to swap. Growing up, the cousins were always in one scrape or another.

Will agreed to go on to Hope with Red.

" For a few days," Red told him, "I traveled with some Texas cowboys who were headed for the Turkey Tracks Ranch. They told me the ranch, east of the Pecos along the caprock, was hiring cowboys. We could get hired on together after we visit my folks."

"After all," Will joked, "didn't we start roping Ma's chickens when we was four or five?"

It was a happy reunion when Red and Will rode into Red's father's ranch near Hope. It was late fall and the cattle were still in good shape. There were many small farms in the settlement irrigated from the Peñasco River. His pa had weaned the calves and put them on some of those nearby fields. The crops had been harvested and the pickings were good.

Red had never seen so many orchards and folks picking apples before winter arrived. When Pa didn't need every hand and the cook to move a bunch of cows, his ma and eleven-year-old sister, Dovie, spent the days peeling, canning, drying and preserving the fruit. The men made a little "apple jack" with the cider.

One day, after their noon meal, Pa announced, "Dinner's over. Get out your pocket-knives boys and peel them apples for Ma. She was good enough to help us this morning, so we want to help her this afternoon."

Pa, on the other hand, was always called by a more pressing task in the corral or at the barn, thus rendering him unable to pitch in and peel. Red noted his pa's escape and wished he had an equally pressing errand. Peeling apples didn't seem like an appropriate task for a tough, young cowboy with his credentials.

Kinsfolk from miles around came for Thanksgiving dinner and stayed a week. That was traditional for the Howell clan. Of course, they all brought food. Each woman had a much-anticipated, mouth-watering speciality and there was a whole lot of good-natured braggin' going on.

Thanksgiving day, Red was a little miffed that he still had to eat at the "second table." It had long been the custom for the adults to eat first — then the kids at the second table. Of course, there were several cousins his age at the table.

I deserve more respect than to eat with the kids.

As each boy swallowed his last piece of whipped-cream-covered sweet potato pie, he headed for the barn. No girls allowed.

Each lad fished out a stash of hidden tobacco. After a few moments of smoking and chewing, they decided it was time to do a little cowboying.

First they saddled the milk cow. She was not one of your proper Jerseys or such. She was range-cow that had a new calf and would maybe give a quart of milk a day with a very thin skim of cream. She was not a docile critter. She was tied to a post with rope around her horns. If she wasn't hobbled by tying her hind feet together, she'd kick you and knock over the milk bucket.

A few of the boys got bucked off because the saddle turned under the cow. Then the saddle had to be rescued from the kicking cow.

At last, the fun went out of that phase of the entertainment and they roped and tied down the calves. They had no stopwatch to see who made the best time, but one of the boys was the "counter." This caused a few disagreements as Red won it all. They were a competitive bunch of cousins and brothers.

Red's pa had tied up a two-year-old colt that he was going to break to ride. The colt was out of his best mare and showed a lot of potential to be a good cow horse.

"Hey, Red," one of the cousins said, "I'll bet you can't ride that colt of your pa's in the round corral."

After a little daring and a lot of bragging, they decided the way for Red to ride the colt was with a loose rope. Just an old cotton rope tied around just behind the horse's front legs, where the cinch of a saddle would be.

Some of the bigger boys, like Will, eared the colt down while Red mounted and got his hands under the rope. He nodded to them that he was ready.

"Let 'er buck," Red yelled.

They turned loose their holds on the horse and headed for the corral fence out of harm's way.

The next thing they knew, Red was airborne. Recounting it later, Will said, "Ol' Red went so high that the robins could have built a nest in his hip pocket before he came down."

It knocked the breath out of Red when he hit the ground.

One of the boys groaned and proclaimed in a loud voice, "Oh, hell, we've killed Red."

The boys rushed over and helplessly fanned Red with their hats.

Red finally opened his eyes. With some effort he sat upright, grabbed his hat with one hand and brushed the dirt off his face with the other. He stood up unsteadily and slapped his hat against his thigh.

"You son of a gun," he croaked. "Catch him again. I'll ride him this time."

The circle of boys opened as Red swayed, got his bearings and took a couple of steps. They all froze when they realized that every man at the party was stationed at the corral fence. Looking like a sheep-killing dog, Red walked over to his pa.

"Pa, thought I'd start that colt for you. I know you're anxious to get him broke."

"Lewis, we'll talk about it later." Red knew that when his pa called him "Lewis," he was in deep trouble.

Chapter Nine

The Real Way to Test a Cowboy

1901-1906

The Turkey Tracks, as everyone called the ranch, was owned by an English syndicate. The wagon was out the year around. There was a crew doctoring worms and branding at any given time.

Red and Will, tall and husky, were sure they could pass for 18 and they knew they were already above average cowboys.

Through the grapevine, Red and Will heard that the Turkey Tracks was hiring. It was December and many of the hands wanted to go home for Christmas.

The boys rode to the ranch and they weren't disappointed. The bookkeeper hired both of them on the spot for the princely salary of $25 a month and keep. The boys could hardly contain their jubilation. $25 a month for a sixteen-year-old, posing as an eighteen-year-old, was big money. Red was offered an additional $5 a month if he'd take the rough string. He agreed without hesitation. Red didn't know it then, but he'd eat a lot of dust that winter.

The boys worked hard and Red steadily gained the respect of the older hands. Many a time Red reached for the saddle horn and picked up a handful of dirt instead, but the men admired his grit, if not his expertise. One old, outlawed horse in the remuda was almost impossible to ride. Red wondered why they didn't just shoot the son-of-a-gun and save a little grass.

The men took to giving Red pointers on how to ride this horse or that.

Red took a beating, but every morning he was up before dawn, ready to rejoin the fight. The time before daylight was bone-chillingly cold. The country east of the Pecos was flatter than a one-sided flapjack and the north wind blew incessantly.

The morning after a particularly brutal day of bronc bustin', one of the cowboys observed Red hobbling out to the corral. He felt so sorry for the boy that he swapped horses with him and got the kinks out of the bronc's back so Red could start the day a little less violently.

Day-after-day, Red was becoming a better "bronc stomper." Finally, Red went to the jigger boss, Randy Weeks, and told him he had to have more money.

"You're not worth what I'm paying you now." Weeks didn't even bother to look up when Red made his request.

"Look, you self-important son-of-a-bitch, that extra $5 you pay me doesn't even cover the cost of buying liniment and salve for my cuts and bruises. Take this job and give it to some other dumb kid. I'm through."

Red stomped away and called to Will, "Get your gear, Will, and let's get out of here."

Will knew he'd just witnessed what the family described as a "Red Howell fit." They didn't happen often, but when they did, it was a sight to see.

Weeks was red as a beet. He clinched his jaw and watched the arrogant young man stomp away. Grudgingly, he stood up and hollered, "Howell, get your sorry self back here."

Red didn't stop walking but he slowed down.

"Howell, we'll give you $10 a month more. I don't want to do it, but we can't afford to lose you right now."

Red stopped. Will whispered, "Come on, Red. That's a good deal."

Red turned and marched back to Randy. He stuck out his hand. "Boss, I sure do appreciate it. I'm sorry I got in such a lather. I hope we can let bygones be bygones."

Randy Weeks returned Red's handshake.

Chapter Ten

Wild, Wild Women

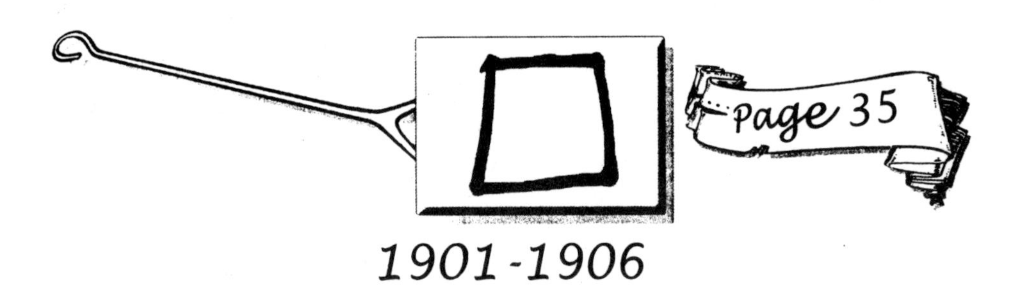

1901-1906

Every month or so, the ranch hands had a free day or two. Finally, the jigger boss thought Red and Will had earned some time off. They were two, happy cowboys.

"Son-of-a-gun," Will proclaimed, "just think of it – we'll ride into the nearest town, have a few drinks and celebrate a little. It has been a long drought."

After a hard day working cattle, they returned to camp, gathered up their clean shirts and Levis and headed to the nearby stock tank to bathe. With a bar of Crystal White soap, they scrubbed vigorously and then washed their clothes so they'd have clean and dry duds when they returned from their spree in town.

Because they were working the west end of the ranch, Roswell the nearest town. The next morning, they were saddled up and on the road at daybreak.

The 35-mile trip took most of the day. Riding along at a jog-trot, Red looked over at Will and asked out of the blue, "Have you ever been to a whorehouse?"

"Nope, Red, I've thought about it a lot, but I never quite figured out how to go about it. Have you?"

Red laughed and said, "Well, I've never been close enough to a town that had a whorehouse since I've got old enough, but I've messed around with a few gals. When we get to Roswell, I think it's about time we tried it. If it don't cost too much, that is."

"I don't want one of those old, cheap chippies. I'd go to a higher class whore, wouldn't you?" Will asked thoughtfully.

"Hell, Will, I don't care how much it costs. I'm getting tired of the other guys on the outfit talking about it and I act like I'm an old hand. It won't hurt nuthin'."

Will snorted. "Well Red, I sure hope it don't hurt." They rode along in silent anticipation, both a little ashamed of their thoughts.

When they finally reached Roswell, they put their horses in a livery stable. They got a room in a fair looking hotel, changed into their good clothes and hit the town feeling like men.

The first bar they went into was full of cowboys. Roswell was a cowboy town. Red and Will ordered a straight shot of whiskey, tossed it down and got talkative.

Red asked a big, burly man on the bar stool next to him, "You cowboy around here somewhere?"

The big man bristled and answered, "No, you dumb, country hick. I don't cowboy, I ranch."

"Didn't mean anything, Mister. You just looked like a cowboy – didn't mean no harm. I'm a cowboy and I'm pretty proud of it." Red said as he looked the man straight in the eye. "We work for the Turkey Tracks over in the caprock country."

"You'd better keep that to yourself, son. This town is in Block country and they're a tough bunch. I'd watch what you do and say around here. They're especially mean about their women."

That left an opening for Red. "Well, we were just having a snort or two before we looked up a good house. Which one would you say had the best girls?"

"Son," the burly man repeated, "as I said, these Block cowboys are mean about their women. They think they own every gal in Roswell. Don't get mixed up with them. They all throw in together like a pack of wolves and they hate the Track hands. They're always spoiling for a fight."

The man paid his bill and walked out without saying another word.

"Friendly bastard, ain't he?" Red observed. "Guess he's a preacher or something and scared of them Block boys. Let's order another shot."

Will had another snort and got brave. "Hell Red, I never saw a Block cowboy before, but it don't scare me none. Does it scare you?"

"Nope," Red answered, "but lets go find a friendlier saloon."

The boys sauntered down the street to another saloon. The atmosphere wasn't that much different from the last place, but the bartender was talkative. After serving them a shot of red-eye, he asked, "You country boys looking to find a woman?"

"Yeah, that's what we came to town for." Trying to look relaxed, Red asked, "Where's the best place to go?"

"Well, by golly, you are in luck young man. I got some girls upstairs. It'll cost you $5, but it'll be the best $5 you'll ever spend."

Will looked at the barman and said, "We'd kinda like to look them over first."

The bartender laughed. "Boy, you're not buying a cow, you're buying an hour with a woman."

"Come on, Will, let's take a chance with whatever he has up there. If we don't like the looks of them, then we'll light a shuck."

"You pay in advance, boys. And, just so you know, the Block cowboys get first choice and you outsiders take what's left over."

"Yeah," Red bristled, "and if the girls prefer us Turkey Track cowhands, then what?"

"You'll get the hell beat out of you. You want a woman or not?" By this time, the bartender's voice had risen and half the men in the room turned and looked at Red and Will.

"We didn't come in here to start a fight. We was just looking for a little fun." Red motioned to Will, who followed him out the door.

"You damned fool, are you trying to get us killed?" Red and Will continued down the road until they were safely away from the saloon. "Let's head for the hotel. I'm hungry as a she-wolf with nine pups. That hooch we been drinking sure gave me an appetite. We can talk this over. I came to town to have a good time, not to start a war."

They reached the hotel without incident and ordered fried chicken and the trimmings. They tucked into it with enthusiasm when it was served.

It was late when they finished. The big meal on top of the whiskey made the boys sleepy. They had ridden all day and drank more redeye in an hour than they usually drank in a month. The upshot was that their quest for women paled in comparison to the draw of the bed and a good night's sleep.

They started up the stairs. Someone called, "Hey, Turkey Track." The boys turned and looked down the stairs. A burly giant of the man stood in the lobby. The boys recognized him as the surly man at the bar they had spoken to at the first saloon they'd visited.

"Come down here," he ordered.

"Looks like trouble, Will," Red whispered.

They walked over to the man. They didn't have a clue what he had in mind, but both were ready in case there were fireworks.

"I've kinda been loose-herding you two tonight and I noticed you crapped out. You two look like good fellows and I don't want you to have to knuckle down to those Block tin-horns. I don't get along with them either. I'm fighting the Blocks for everything I have and I think I'm losing ground on the cattle-end of things. On the other hand, I own a few businesses here in town – this hotel for one and a couple of whore houses.

"You two go on up to your room. I'll send up a couple of girls who know all the tricks and you can go back to the Tracks and do a little bragging."

He continued. "I've devirgined a lot of women, but I've never been a part of keeping a couple of boys from losing theirs. This first time is on the house. Next time will cost you. I'm even going to throw in another room so you boys can have a little privacy."

Red and Will stood there with their mouths open, not knowing what to do or say. Finally Red stuttered, "Mister, we surely appreciate this more than you'll ever know and we'll gratefully take you up on the deal if it isn't a joke. We're pretty green. By the way, how'd you know we were virgins?"

"I've been down that road, boys. It's been a long, long time ago but I remember it like it was yesterday and you'll never forget this night as long as you live." He turned and went out the front door.

Shaking their heads, Red and Will looked at each other. "I think he meant it. If it's some kind of joke, it's our fault for being too damned green. I'll take the new room and keep my pistol nearby and you do the same, Will. If you hear shooting, come as quick as you can 'cause I'll be in a lot of trouble."

Red went into his room, pulled off his boots, sat on the bed and waited. He was about ready to take off his 10-gallon, Texas-creased Stetson and lock the door when he heard a faint knock.

With his pistol in one hand, he opened the door with the other. There stood one of the prettiest, blonde-headed women he'd ever seen. She was wearing a red, silk dress, cut mighty low in front. He knew instantly that she was a whore and not the kind of gal he'd take home to ma. He was ready.

She reached up, took off his Stetson, set it on the dresser and ruffled his red, curly hair. "You won't be needing a hat tonight." She took his hand and led him to the bed.

When Red awoke the next morning he discovered that the blonde-headed woman was gone. In her wake, she left the cloying odor of cheap perfume.

What the hell have I done? Red wanted a bath and he wanted it now. He pulled on his pants, shirt, hat and boots and stormed down to the lobby. A sleepy-eyed clerk had probably seen the girls leave hours ago.

Damn, I hope that clerk don't want his money back . He don't know it was a gratis deal and I'm not going to tell him.

"Feller," Red said, "how do you go about getting a bath in this establishment?"

"The bath is at the end of your hall. It'll cost you four-bits extra for hot water. Do you want it now?"

"Hell, yes," Red stormed. "If I wanted to take a bath tomorrow, I'd a said so." He pulled two quarter-dollars out of his pocket and placed them on the counter.

The clerk rang a bell and immediately an elderly black man appeared with two huge buckets of steaming water.

"Mr Howell, Nate here works and lives on tips alone. Don't forget that."

"I'll be damned. If you're going to run my business full-time, come up and wash my back when I get in the tub."

The little clerk seemed to shrivel up and the young man towering over him looked like he was about to throw a Red Howell fit.

Red followed Nate back up the stairs, taking one more look at the room to be sure the gal was gone.

The room with the bath was like none Red had ever seen.

Lordy, lordy, you could water a hundred head of cows in that trough. It's sure good that I know how to swim.

Nate, four-bits richer, closed the door gently as he left. Red shucked off his clothes and gingerly immersed himself in the hot water. There was a bar of the nicest smelling soap in a dish and the scent reminded him again of the blonde. He used the soap vigorously, trying to get a lather in the alkali water.

He stretched out his lanky 6'3" frame and soaked in luxurious peace. He recalled the various places he'd taken a bath: a number-three zinc wash tub, the Guadalupe River in Texas and every stock tank between Kerrville and Roswell.

This morning, he felt like a man of the world.

Leaning out of the tub, he opened the door and yelled down the hall, "Hey Will, do you want me to save my bath water for you?"

Some of the cousins. They don't look this good most of the time.

Chapter Eleven

The Homestead at Four Wells

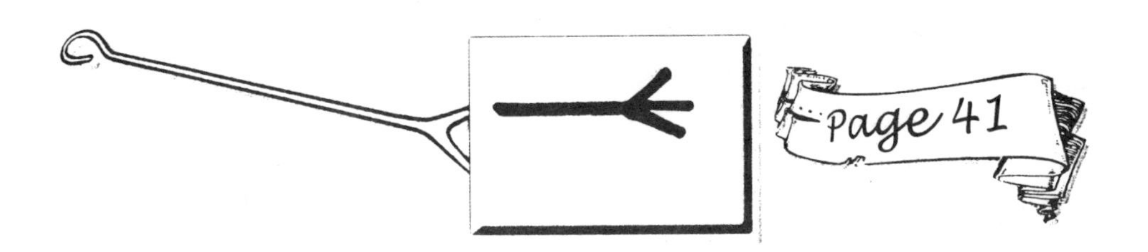

At the end of a long two-day trip, Red and Will rode into Hope. They were returning from the from the railhead at Roswell. The boys had helped bring in a herd for shipment. Some of the cattle had gone to Montana, others were routed to the Mid-West wheat fields where the Turkey Tracks syndicate had holdings. Red had managed to save a good-sized sack of cash. He'd accumulated it from his wages and money he'd won at ranch rodeos, matched horse races and poker. Black Jack and craps were his games and he won a fair amount off the other cowboys around the campfire at night.

"You know, Will," Red turned in the saddle and said, "I'm lucky at cards, but I sure ain't lucky with women. Oh, well, someday the right one will come along wearing a red dress." Red hadn't forgotten the blonde-headed gal in Roswell.

"Will, you know, I've got a mind to file a homestead claim and build myself a little shack to prove up on it."

Will had heard it before. "You couldn't drive a nail if your life depended on it. You're hell on horseback but I don't reckon you can build a shack on horseback."

Red chuckled, "As much as it pains me to admit it, you're right. I'll have to find somebody handy with a saw and hammer. I sure wouldn't want to live in anything I built. It'd be dangerous and like an old, blind horse: It wouldn't look too good."

Their Hope homecoming couldn't have been better. The entire Howell clan put the big pot in the little one and had a barbeque and dance. The fiddle music, provided by musicians from the Lewis family who lived on the adjoining ranch, filled the air. Everyone in the Lewis family played some instrument and they were all good musicians.

One thing Red thought he could do on foot was dance. He'd picked up steps here and there in neighboring towns at shindigs and at saloons on his trips to Roswell from the Turkey Tracks.

After a vigorous reel, Red hobbled over to a bale of hay, flopped down and fanned himself with his hat.

"You're quite a dancer there, Red." The cowboy next to him observed.

"Truth be told, I'm not much of a dancer but I sure do like to hold the girls. Of course, these here are nice girls, so there isn't too much holdin'" Red silently reflected on the fact that these women were a whole different breed from the ones that he and Will had been chousing during their years on the Turkey Tracks.

"Yep." The other cowboy seemed to read his mind. "You'll be looking into the barrel of a 12-gauge if you don't mind your manners here. Unless you're ready to jump the broomstick, you'd be well advised to keep your distance."

Like most Westerners, Red was well aware of the Homestead Act of 1862. He knew he could claim a quarter section — 160 acres of land — and own it when he proved up on it after five years. Five years seemed like enough time to make the required improvements that would validate his claim. There was plenty of unclaimed land around the area he planned to homestead and he could use it as additional grazing land for his cattle. Nothing was fenced, but you'd better be a cowboy and on the lookout. A whole lot of men were stocking their own homestead claims with a rope and a hot iron.

The land Red chose was in the foothills of the Guadalupe Mountains on a creek that ran through the 160 acres. Red called the creek and the ranch "Four Wells." He branded CO/ and kept adding to his small herd with his pa's help and by mavericking many of the unbranded, unclaimed wild cattle in this remote area.

He built corrals in the Mexican style by setting two, upright posts and stacking limbs between them. He built the fences up five or six feet high. The fence was free if you didn't count your labor.

Red lucked out. He only had to dig about twenty feet before he hit water. The well was cribbed with the same kind of timbers he used for the corrals, so it wouldn't cave in.

His dream of having a windmill over the well was finally realized. It had to be hauled by wagon from Carlsbad in pieces and assembled by hand. He had to have help setting it up. When it was finally finished, he was proud to have running water pumped by the wind.

From dawn until dusk, Red labored, hating the menial, back-breaking work that no cowboy should have to do. Nevertheless, he knew that he had to make the improvements to be able to claim the Four Wells as his own.

The shack was the thorn in his side. He knew he needed shelter and a place to live while he ran the ranch. He built a small frame and covered it with canvas. He moved in wooden crates to use for storage, a rickety, homemade table and a bed. He used a couple of wooden horse-shoe kegs for chairs. A small, sheepherder's stove never quite kept the shack warm enough in the winter. Red cooked over a campfire outside in the summer.

Red used a Dutch oven to bake biscuits and he killed a deer when he needed meat. There was generally venison stew and beans simmering year around. His specialty was Garlic Stew with Irish potatoes, cloves of garlic and salt pork.

All his life, he'd seen his ma make corn bread, biscuits, and light bread. "Red," she'd explained, "light bread has yeast in it and biscuits have baking powder."

If he happened to be in the house when she was cooking, she often gave a running commentary of what she was doing and why she was doing it. She filled her monologues with humor and Red enjoyed it. Unless he was home with the croup or nursing an injury, the two of them seldom spent time alone together. Now, Red realized how much those times meant to him and what she was trying to do. He'd enjoyed the sound of her voice, but he hadn't paid much attention to what she was actually saying. He realized that she had foreseen a time when he'd have to do for himself and she'd tried to give him the tools he'd need. Some-how, he'd never envisioned a time when he'd have to cook for himself or starve.

Biscuits were one of the staples of his diet. He fried the dough in bacon grease — you could knock a bull down with one of them. Nevertheless, the biscuits were edible and filling.

The bean pot was always on. The gyp water wasn't compatible with bean cooking. The longer you cooked them, the harder they got. After the rains, the little Four Wells creek ran and the water was soft. Beans cooked in water from the stream were better. Red added spice to his bean pot with a handful of garlic, a dried, red chili pepper or two and some salt pork. After a hard day of riding, a hot bowl of beans seemed was a royal feast.

Red liked cream in his coffee, but he was damned if he was going to break a cow to milk. He packed his milk in on his infrequent trips to town. When he punched a hole in the can, he recited:

Carnation milk, best in the land,
Comes to the table in a little red can.
No teats to squeeze, no tail to switch,
Just jab a hole in the son-of-a-bitch.

The food and shelter of the small tent-house attracted varmints. Red set traps for the mice and pack rats. The profound silence at night was often punctuated by the satisfying sound of a trap snapping shut; a squeal, and the dull thud of metal on flesh. Occasionally, late at night, Red stumbled into a trap. The transition from sleepy peace to sudden pain evinced the full fury of a Red Howell fit. In spite of the hazards, the traps kept the rodent population in check.

As bad as the rats and mice were, the rattlesnakes were a worse problem. They'd come into the house hunting for rodents. Red always lit the kerosene lamp before he ventured out at night, but several times a rattlesnake had been coiled on the floor of his shack between his bed and the lamp.

Red vowed that he'd get a real house built and it would damned well be snake proof.

Eventually, Cyrus Bauer, a down-and-out carpenter with a nagging wife and a bunch of kids approached Red and offered his house-building services at a price Red could afford to pay.

Cy built corner stones from rock and cement and put in a couple additional pilings. Four stout timbers formed the support for the rest of the structure and Cy worked steadily to make the basic house a reality.

Red helped Cy all he could, which is to say he didn't help much until it was time to raise the roof. At that point, Red had to pitch in to get the job done. He reluctantly turned his two saddle horses out to pasture and presented himself to Cy.

"Okay, I'm ready to get domestic. What do you need me to do?"

The two-room house was made of rough lumber and the men worked together under Cy's supervision to build the trusses in place for the roof. They tied the trusses together with boards and finally tacked the corrugated tin roof over the whole structure.

Cy wasn't a finish carpenter, but he did manage to put in the store-bought door and three windows. The west wind still got in, but Red figured he'd stuff a rag or two in the cracks and it would be snug and warm in the winter.

Like a kid with a playhouse, Red was itching to show off his new castle but there wasn't anyone to show it to. Red often rode out, but guests to Four Wells were few and far between.

Over time he'd made the acquaintance of a pair of old bachelors. Kinnebrew and Weedle O'Connor lived eight miles southwest of Red's place. Red didn't know much about them except that they were from back east somewhere and they didn't want to talk about their former lives.

Kinnebrew played a concertina and the men seemed to be well educated. Each brother had built his own one-room claim shack and they always seemed pleased when Red stopped by for a visit. They ran a few head of cattle and Red was happy to give them a hand when they needed it. He taught them how to re-leather the sucker rod on their windmill and showed them how to trap the coyotes that preyed on their small flock of chickens.

Red's visits were a good excuse to play a few tunes on the concertina and Red was always pleased at the end of his visits when the brothers insisted that he take a dozen, fresh eggs.

Another neighbor, Eb Ately, lived up in the mountains. Eb ran a couple hundred cows. He never took a bath unless he got caught in a rain storm and even then, he didn't relish getting washed off.

Eb was the world's biggest liar. He could not tell the truth. Red heard he'd had a family at one time, but the scuttlebutt was that his wife and kids took off. Eb's wife couldn't take the kind of life Eb offered, so she loaded the wagon, hitched up the horses and took off for Carlsbad. Eb hadn't seen her since and, as a result, he hated all women and most men. His tale tales grew wilder and crazier as time passed.

Red rode by one day looking for some cows he couldn't account for. Their tracks led him to the rough country where Eb ranched. The only water, pumped by a windmill into a dirt tank in a fenced lot, was near his house.

Eb and Red howdied and shook and talked about the weather.

"Say, Eb," Red asked, "have you seen a couple of my cows around here lately? I'm out an old brindle cow and calf and a nice white-faced cow just ready to calve. I'm afraid they couldn't find water."

The old fellow was silent for a minute and then said, "Yeah, Red, they came by a day or two ago. I didn't water them, but I let them lick salt awhile."

Red never knew what happened to the brindle cow's calf for sure, but as he rode off, he saw a small, fresh hide, hair-side in, on the corral fence.

He found the cows not far from Eb's place badly drawn for water. He rode along, driving the cows, and thinking about the man.

Eb sure leads a lonesome, solitary life. It's no wonder his wife left him. I can't believe he's taken to telling new folks that his wife and kids were brutally killed by Indians.

Everybody knew Eb's wife had left him. They figured he couldn't face it any more so he made up an increasingly elaborate story about what happened to his family.

Lately, Eb was saying the Indians had jumped the family one day on their the way home from town. Eb claimed to have shot a lot of them, but he ran out of shells, so he jumped on one of the draft horses and rode for help with the Indians in hot pursuit.

"They ran me into a box canyon. There was no way out and I was out of bullets."

"What happened then, Eb?"

"Well, by God, they killed me." That was what he always answered.

Red finally rode into sight of his homestead. The thrill of seeing his house, corrals and windmill surged through him. He was proud of what he'd accomplished with the months and months of hard work.

Damn, I need to get out of here and make money to buy more

cows and lay claim to some more country. I sure as hell don't want to end up like the old bachelors or old Eb Ately.

Red had received a letter from his brother, Jim, bragging about his job in Arizona. Jim wrote that he wanted Red to join him because the ranch boss was always looking for good hands.

Mulling over the idea, Red decided that it was time to make some money and find a wife. The right woman wouldn't mind living out here in his new house. For now, he'd hire somebody to live on the Four Wells and take care of it and he'd go work for wages for a couple of years.

The first chance he got, Red rode down to Seven Rivers. He stayed with Aunt Elsie and Uncle Landy, Will's parents.

"Will is working near Loving," his uncle Landy explained. "He's living on a big ranch and he's fixing to marry."

"I'm sure happy for Will, Uncle Landy, but I'll miss my old running buddy. We had a lot of fun together."

In Seven River, Red found a man and his wife, Don and Effie Brown, who had just arrived from Texas with twenty-head of cattle.

"We droughted out," Don explained. "We had to let our homestead go back to the government. Right now, we're looking for a place to run our cattle so we can start to get back on our feet."

"I'll tell you what," Red offered. "You take care of my place and my cattle and you can run your herd and build it back up. I'll give you $15 a month to cover your other expenses."

"Red, that sounds like it would suit us fine. Let's shake on it."

Red stayed another month on his Four Wells Ranch making sure Don knew everything he needed to know about the country and cattle.

Dan was handy with a hammer and he built a chicken coop and a fenced pen to keep out the coyotes, bobcats and other varmints that had a taste for chicken.

Red brought a milk cow and some chickens back from a trip to his parent's ranch. Effie was in hog heaven.

For the past few years, Red had kept the wolf from the door by trapping coyotes. He got $ .50 for a dried, stretched hide.

Don savvied trapping as well. This would give the Browns a small but steady income.

Red was reassured that Don and Effie would be able to live fairly comfortably and so be more likely to stay for the next couple of years. His pa said he'd ride over from time to time to check on things. In the meantime, Red would be able to build up a nest egg.

On a clear, cool fall day, Red saddled up, told everyone adiós, and lit a shuck for Arizona. He traveled through the Guadalupe Mountains, down Dog Canyon to Crow Flat. He loosely planned his route so he'd be near a ranch at the end of the day where he could spend the night with ranchers he knew.

As he made his way down the trail, he thought about his herd. He'd sold his steer calves to a fellow on Black River near Carlsbad. Red kept his heifers for replacement.

He'd taken the money he'd made and put it in the bank at Hope, which was owned by a fellow named Gage.

Red looked at the road ahead and felt a sense of freedom he hadn't experienced in a long time. He marveled at being footloose and fancy free with a couple of dollars in his pocket and a new adventure ahead of him. When he had a stake, he'd head back to his own place, but in the meantime, he'd see some country.

After leaving El Paso and the Rio Grande Valley, he headed due west to a little town called Hachita, owned by the Diamond A Cattle Company. The Diamond A owned land from Silver City to the Mexican border. They ran thousands of good cattle and hundreds of horses. They employed cowboys from all over the West.

Drinking at the old saloon in Hachita that night, Red found some new drinking companions when they discovered they all had friends in common. They traded information and stories on their friends and enjoyed a companionable evening as they tied one on.

Chapter Twelve

Cowboying on the Diamond A

1909 - 1910

Red had heard cowboys talk about the Diamond A Ranch all his life. It was known for its enormous size, covering a large part of Southwestern New Mexico.

The cattle were wild and the horses were rank, but the cowboys were even ranker.

The bosses who ran the Diamond A didn't ask for pedigree papers when they hired on a hand. If you looked like you could weather a storm, you were hired. Red must have fit that description because he was hired the next day and assigned to a wagon working up in the Burro Mountains near Silver City.

Two other cowboys were hired that day. That night at the bar, he heard one of them say that they were from Texas. Red suspected, by the way they evaded the questions the other cowboys asked, that all was not up to snuff.

"We crossed the Rio Grande at Langtry, rode through Mexico to Columbus and headed up to Hatchita from there." Red heard one of the Texans describe his trip to another man at the bar.

Later, Red realized that he may have left them with the impression that his situation was similar to theirs because it was obvious that he was traveling light. Red didn't try to disabuse them of the idea that they all had something in common. They were rough hombres and Red wanted to get along with them.

The next morning, Red introduced himself. "Howdy, it looks like we're headed the same direction. They call me Red."

"Pleased to meet you. I'm Butch and this here rough looking fellow is my pard, Len."

"I'm going over to the company store." Red stated. "You fellows going that way, too?"

"Yep, I need to put some gear together. I reckon I need a bed tarp, a soogan, some work clothes and such," Len said.

"That mostly covers what I need, too," Red replied.

With their bundles of newly purchased supplies, Red, Butch and Len headed back to the Diamond A Ranch. The next morning the three of them tied their gear on Diamond A pack horses and headed north. They were nine miles out of Hachita by sun-up and stopped at a windmill to water their horses and themselves.

"This looks like good ranching country," Red observed as the men rested for a few minutes.

His traveling companions grunted in reply.

Hell, Red though, wouldn't it be just dandy if I was traveling with a couple of cowboys who could actually talk? It sure would make traveling more interesting.

After a bit, Red stood up, stretched, walked over and tightened the cinch, and got on his horse. He took the lead rope of the pack horse, dallied it around his saddle horn and rode north.

Red briefly thought that riding away from Len and Butch was not such a good idea. He had that same prickly feeling he'd had when he rode away from his grandfather nearly ten-years-ago. The old man said farewell by training his rifle on Red's back, yelling all the while that he was just itching to shoot.

The pack horse Red was leading had all their gear. Nevertheless, he figured they were all going the same place and the taciturn Texans would be following along sooner or later.

Leading a pack horse slowed Red down and he didn't travel as far that day as he hoped he would. He made camp and about sundown, the two "friendly bastards," as he thought of them, finally rode into camp.

They unsaddled their horses, hobbled them and came over to the camp fire that Red was tending.

Red filled the coffee pot from a canteen and opened a can of Arbuckle's coffee. He threw a handful of ground coffee into the boiling water.

The two saddle tramps just stood and watched. Red set out three cups and a can of Carnation milk. Red poured himself a cup of coffee, added a liberal amount of sugar and milk and hunkered down by the fire. With a sigh of satisfaction, he savored the rich, sweet brew thinking: This must be what the nectar of the gods tastes like. Red relaxed and grinned, marveling at how good the world seemed and how at ease he felt in it.

"Red, you want me to fry some bacon?" Butch asked.

"Yeah," Red replied without any expression. "If you want to eat, you'll cook it. I ain't wet-nursing no cowboys tonight."

"Suits me," Butch said. "You ain't never et no bacon as good as I cook."

Butch pulled the frying pan and bacon out of the pannier. He raked some coals out of the fire and set the pan on the coals. He pulled a large knife out of the sheath on his waist, cut slices off the slab of bacon and dropped them into the pan. The bacon jumped and sizzled when it hit the hot metal.

Butch rewrapped the slab of bacon in the greasy paper and returned it to the sack that also contained a few onions and a dozen sourdough biscuits. The cook at Headquarters had packed their grub and it looked like he had done a good job.

The men relaxed around the small fire. The smell of smoke, coffee and frying bacon mingled with the familiar tang of the horses, saddles and damp blankets in the high desert air. The conversation was desultory. Red asked no questions. He replied if asked a direct question, but other than that, he was silent, except to brag on the bacon and onion sandwiched in a sourdough biscuit that had been fried in the bacon grease. The men washed down their food with steaming coffee.

As the sun crested the horizon the next morning, the men were following a wagon road toward the Burro Mountains. The tracks in the road told them that a couple of wagons and a lot of horses had headed up the trail before them and they knew they were traveling the right direction.

When they finally saw the Diamond A chuck wagon and the bed wagon, they knew they had arrived at their destination.

There were thirteen cowboys and three times that many horses in the remuda.

Red rode up asked, "Who's the wagon boss?"

A big, rawboned Texas-looking hombre stood up.

"I'm Jim Stephenson." The man had confidence and an air of

authority that marked him as the person cracking the whip in this camp. "What's your name, cowboy?"

"I'm Red Howell from over Carlsbad way. We were sent up from Hatchita yesterday."

Red stepped off his sweaty horse, still holding the lead rope of the pack horse.

"Did you bring any mail" Stephenson asked, "or any word from the big boss?"

"Here's the stuff the boss-man sent," Red replied. He handed Stephenson an envelope.

"This is Len and Butch," Red nodded toward his traveling companions. "Where do we throw our gear and where do you want our horses? Man, I didn't realize how hungry I was 'til I smelled that good cooking."

Red knew it didn't hurt to honey-up the cook right from the very first. The way to the old Turkey Tracks cook's heart was a pint, which in this case he didn't have. Nevertheless, in the future, he'd try to keep the 'ol cookie supplied when he could, if a pint proved to be what this cook preferred. When it came to his stomach, Red looked ahead.

Red liked Stevenson. He turned out to be a good wagon boss. Most of the men he worked with were capable and amiable. The country they were working was in the mountains. It was quite different from any place he'd ever worked, although in some ways it reminded him of his own Four Wells Ranch in the foothills of the Guadalupe Mountains.

The Diamond A cowboys worked from can-see to can't-see. The daylight to dark schedule was hard on the horses, and the cowboys usually changed mounts around mid-day when they took a little break to eat a some jerky and have a cool drink of creek water.

The wages were fair. Red was saving his money for the most part. Every once in a while some of his wages went to a spree in town but he was constantly aware that he must stock his ranch as soon as he could.

In his work, he was learning more and more about a cow. In a way, that surprised Red. His family on both his mother's and father's side of the family had been in the cattle business forever.

What he was learning was that each outfit and each boss worked differently. If it all worked well, Red observed that success came from letting the country you were working dictate how you ran a roundup. Being hidebound in your ways and not paying attention to all the conditions could result in disastrous decisions.

Red enjoyed learning little tricks from the other hands. The cowboys came from all over the Southwest and each had a different slant on things. Red's attention paid off and he was pleased that he was considered to be one of the best hands around.

Almost every payday, the cowboys went into Silver City and tied one on. The next day on the drive, the celebrants rode with painful hangovers and grouched about headaches that threatened to split open the skull at any minute. What the heck. That's what a cowboy's life was all about.

Len and Butch had the habit of unrolling their beds quite a distance from the other men.

When asked about it, Red commented dryly, "Well, they just ain't socially inclined."

One morning when Cookie beat the triangle to call the men to breakfast, Len and Butch didn't show up. Their bed rolls had not been rolled up and tied so they'd be ready to pitch into the bed wagon after breakfast.

Pedro, one of the horse wranglers, reported that Len and Butch had tied their horses in a nearby thicket the previous night.

"I'd say from the sign," Pedro told the boss with the men listening, "that they sneaked out of camp last night sometime. They led their horses away, saddled them and lit a shuck."

"Segundo," Jim ordered, "you take over the drive. I'm riding into Silver City."

Jim, like Red, had pegged Len and Butch as shady characters.

"Something about them didn't ring true," Jim explained to Segundo. "For one thing, you know cowboys love to brag about all the outfits they've worked for. They're always figuring out who they know in common and swapping tales and news. Those two didn't have much to say and they didn't bother to join in with the other hands."

"Yep," Segundo said, "that's true. So, what are you going to do?"

"I don't rightly know," Jim replied, "but I guess I'll ride on into town and have a little talk with the sheriff. I sure wouldn't feel right if something bad happened and I hadn't bothered to inform the local law of our missing cowhands. It probably won't come to anything, but I'll rest easier."

When Jim arrived at the Sheriff's office in Silver City, he dismounted and tied his horse to the hitching rail. He went in and told his tale to Sheriff McDonald.

"I'm much obliged to you for coming in."

The sheriff handed Jim a pile of Wanted Posters. "Look through these and see if anybody looks familiar."

"I'll be damned," Jim exclaimed. "Here they are. Look at this. It says they killed two men in an attempted bank robbery in San Angelo. And that's not all, Sheriff. There's a dead-or-alive award of $1000 for them. Man, but that's a lot of money!"

Jim and the sheriff looked at each other and immediately had the same thought. The First National Bank of Silver City.

"You said they left your camp last night and their tracks indicated that they were heading for Silver City? Let's mosey down to the bank." The sheriff picked up his rifle, ushered Jim out the door and locked the office and the two men headed for the bank.

"We can let the president of the bank know that there may be some trouble heading his way."

That night, deputies were posted inside the bank, covering both the front and back. They weren't surprised when the doors opened and in came Len and Butch. Without firing a shot, the deputies captured the wanted men. After the outlaws had been relived of their firearms and handcuffed, they were marched to the jail.

There was a lot of cussing and struggling as the deputies herded Len and Butch, but soon enough they were double-locked in the jail and armed guards were posted around the building to head off any attempts at a jail break.

Now, the question arose as to who would get the reward money. Jim figured he should have the biggest share since his ride to town directly resulted in the positive identification and capture of the killers. And, to top it off, Jim reminded everyone who would listen, that contrary to what could have happened, nobody had been hurt.

Jim bought a couple of bottles of "Old Rot Gut," as the boys called it, to take back to the camp so the men could have a little celebration around the campfire.

A chill ran up Jim's back as he returned to the cow camp. He prayed the jailer didn't botch it and let them escape. Butch and Len would have certainly realized that Jim had put the kibosh on their to plans to rob the bank. If they got out, they'd probably head to Mexico, but not before they exacted some revenge on Jim and the Diamond A hands.

Several uneventful weeks in the roundup camp had gone by and Jim and the cowboys had finally started to relax. Eventually, the cowboys who had a day off headed to Silver City and came back with the news that the outlaws had indeed attempted an escape. Both men had been shot and killed in the process, thereby cheating the hangman.

On hearing the news, the whole camp and especially Jim let out a collective sigh of relief. The all considered the deaths happy news. The whole camp had been uneasy with the knowledge that a pair of cold-blooded killers knew their day-to-day habits and in all likelihood wished them harm.

Jim got most of the reward money. He bought each cowboy in his outfit a new Stetson and planned to squirrel away the rest for a rainy day.

Later, after the men had a few snorts of booze, paid for with the reward money, Red finally said what had been on his mind.

"Hey, you gringo, I think I got chingered. I'm the one who brought those men up here. I was responsible for them. They could have shot me in the back while I was leading them here. Dammit, Jim don't you agree?"

"Hell no, Red. They should go ahead and hang you for throwing in with those outlaws," Jim joked. "I guess I'll turn you in and see what you're worth. Hell, I might get enough money to buy that ranch I want."

My place at Four Wells.

That's Earl Howell on the horse.

Chapter Thirteen

Winter Bronc Stomping on the Diamond A

1910 - 1911

It was the middle of November and the camp men were back at the Diamond A. Most of the drifting cowboys left at the end of the roundup. Like Red, the few drifters who remained on the ranch were good hands at breaking and training young horses.

Horses were raised to work the cattle. The three-year-old colts that were to be broken and trained as cow-horses were kept through the winter months at the headquarters.

They broke and trained the young horses in the round corrals. When the men got the colts snapped out, they took them outside to work the cattle which were kept around the headquarters in small pastures of 10 or 15 sections. There was a registered herd that produced bulls which were turned out each spring with the cows for the next year's calf crop. Ranching is all about planning for the next year and it has to be carefully managed.

Putting the bulls out too early or leaving them in the pastures too long produced a calf in the early fall or winter. In Diamond A country, the forage became increasingly poor as winter came on. A cow having a calf at that time had a hard time producing enough milk for her offspring.

Usually, in that part of the country, they put the bulls out in June and the calves were born in February and March. The boss liked to have a calf eight or nine months old, ready to wean from its mother so it could be shipped in its prime from late October to early November.

Buyers contracted the cattle for so much per head in May and set a delivery date, agreeable for both the ranch and the buyer, for a date in the fall. This was payday for the Diamond A.

Cattle ranching is a year-around business. Even with careful planning everything depends on the weather. It was a crap-shoot and Red liked it. The gamble intrigued him. He scanned the sky more than any man since Noah. The only difference was that Red was hoping for a cloud, but Noah wasn't.

Ranching was different from Texas where his family had ranched for generations. It was even different here than his Four Wells homestead. He loved learning the different approaches each honcho used when working cattle. He was storing up all these observations for his future.

Red was in hog heaven working with the young broncs. He never tired of the thrill of getting on a raw bronc to match his skill against the horse's. Some of these horses from the Lower Gray had seen few men during their three years of freedom on the open range before they were brought into headquarters to be broken. The men put a rein on them and they were used for what they were bred to be: cow horses.

The man in charge at the Gray had plenty of savvy on blood lines, knowledge about line-breeding and inbreeding. It showed on the colts when they were brought into the huge set of corrals at the headquarters. The horse breakers drew straws to see who chose first and on down the line.

All the hands got along well and there was a whole lot of joshing going on over the drawing.

The horses had been at Headquarters about five days. This was a time for them to get used to people, corrals, hay, grain and captivity,

Red had his eye on five or six that he wanted badly to cut out for himself.

His first pick was a big, roan colt, well built and large enough to carry a man all day. The cowboys who had lucked out on the draw didn't choose him. Red was delighted, he was now a big, long-legged man tipping the scales at near 200 pounds and above 6'4". He needed a big horse.

Some of the colts were not big bodied and Red sure didn't like to ride all day with his legs hanging straight down. He chose the horses with bigger barrels and larger bones. They would be harder to ride because of their size, but Red tried to keep them calm so they wouldn't buck. He didn't need to show off his riding ability at the expense of a young, green horse that could easily be made to get his head down and try to throw his rider just for show.

The colts were coming along fine, Red thought. He was not in charge – just one of the boys, but the big boss had his eye on him. Red liked to take time with each colt he rode.

It was not unusual to see Red in the corrals by daylight, rubbing down the colt to be ridden first that day. Red liked it better if he arrived at the corrals before the other bronc stompers got up. He had it all to himself and if he threw a Red Howell fit, he could stomp and cuss without some of the other hands making comments about his temper.

They all respected Red. They were older men and had more experience but they were not better riders than the redheaded kid. Moreover, they had seen him deck a guy at the saloon in Hachita, and nobody wanted to look like that cowboy did after Red finished with him.

Red had singled out a gal from one of the ranches in the Animas Valley. Her family had a small place in comparison to the Diamond As. They raised good, white-faced cattle. She attended all the dances at the nearby ranches but never the dances at the saloon. When Red rode over to her parent's ranch, he led a horse for her to ride. They were always chaperoned to the dance and even church doings by either her father or a brother.

This bothered Red. He wanted to talk to her in private, maybe make a little love to her, but the occasion never happened. He wondered why her folks didn't trust him – he knew a good woman when he saw one and he damned sure didn't want to smear her reputation.

Red wanted to share his thoughts with her. The time was fast approaching when the wagons would light out for the spring roundup and he wouldn't see her again until after they finished branding the yearlings they'd missed in the fall.

He never got a chance to ask her to wait for him but somehow he knew she would.

He was badly fooled. One day just before the wagons were despatched to their spring destinations, Red rode over to Margaret's dad's ranch fully intending to tell her about his little homestead in the Guadalupes and ask her to share it with him.

When he arrived, he saw a horse tied to the hitching rail that wasn't wearing the Diamond A brand.

Who the hell? Red walked up the steps to the porch and knocked on the front door. Margaret rose from the settee where she cuddled up with a striking looking, older man. Now he knew that he wasn't the only man trying to build a smoke under her. This fellow was getting the job done.

"I came by to take you to the barbeque over at Darnell's Ranch.

Want to go?" Red asked.

She turned a rosy face in the direction of the man on the settee, "Oh Red, I can't go with you. I've been asked already and I'm going with Percy."

A Red Howell fit was long overdue and he threw a dandy.

"What do you mean? You're going with that city slicker who's sitting there looking like the cat that ate the canary? You're my gal and you know it." Red stormed back-and-forth across the porch.

"Red, I guess I should have told you. My papa arranged my marriage with Percy here when I was in my early teens. I always knew I'd marry him when I got older. I'm older now, so we're planning our wedding."

"Well, I'll be damned," Red stormed, "all this time you've been cuddling up to me, expecting me to kiss you and stuff. I've been a gentleman and respected you and now I realize you'd'a gone with me to the brush at the drop of a hat."

Margaret's face was even redder now and if looks could have killed, she'd have been pleased to see Red drop dead right on the spot.

The man on the settee finally got up. Red thought: What, that guy is pretty puny. Must'a doggied some time back. I ought'a beat the hell out of him.

Then Red realized that Margaret's beau wasn't getting up to fight. He seemed indifferent to the whole situation.

I can't believe the sorry son-of-a-bitch isn't even going to try to protect her reputation. I'd never let anybody talk to my gal like that, especially when I was fixin' to marry her.

"To hell with the whole thing," Red exclaimed. "Margaret, you ain't got no more conscience than a cow in a stampede and your beau here ain't worth the powder to blow him up. I'm starting to think you two make a real good pair."

A couple tears ran down Margaret's cheek as her soon-to-be husband looked on. Red stomped off the porch. As mad as he was, Red sensed that Margaret was going to have a tough row to hoe and he felt like going back and taking her in his arms. He imagined himself fending off the puny Percy with one hand while ardently embracing Margaret with the other and the ridiculous image brought a rueful smile to his lips.

No gal had ever two-timed him before and he wasn't happy that he'd been such a fool for her. On the other hand, he sure wasn't going to let this eat at him. He untied both horses, got on his mount and felt silly as hell, racing off from her house with an empty saddle.

As he rode away, he looked longingly at the livestock. Maybe I let those good, white-faced cows get the best of me, he admitted to himself. I sure wanted to take a bunch of them back to Four Wells, with Margaret thrown in to boot.

Red didn't go to the barbeque. He sneaked into Headquarters, unsaddled both horses, and turned them out in the horse pasture. The bunk house was quiet and empty. Red undressed and went to bed.

This relationship business was more tiring than working all day with a bunch of wild cows. His only regret, as he nodded off to sleep, was that he had paid a Mexican gal in Hachita fifty cents to wash, starch and iron his only good, white shirt. He'd worn it when he'd gone to court Margaret.

"That was four bits totally wasted," he mumbled.

Mama and Ruth

Crazy
Margaret

Chapter Fourteen

Arizona, Here Comes Red Howell

Spring, 1911

The spring works at the Diamond A were over. The cowboys shipped the yearlings they'd missed in the roundup the fall before. Red was free.

"I won't be available through the summer to range-brand and doctor worms," he told Mr. MacFarland, the jigger boss on a clear May morning. "I'm going to go see my brother, Jim, over in Arizona. Jim works for the Three Cs. He calls the outfit the 'Cherry Cows.'"

"Why, Red," Mac protested, "I need you this summer. There aren't many hands who savvy the country like you do. I was kinda depending on you to show some of these new cowboys around."

"I'm sure sorry, Mr. MacFarland. I like working here and I can tell you that I've learned a whole bunch from you. The thing is, my brother has been looking for me to show up at his place for a couple of years now. I'd better go, or he's going to give up on me."

"Are your going to work for the Triple Cs?" Mac asked.

"Just for the summer," Red answered. "Then I'm going back to my little place near Carlsbad. I've saved up enough money to buy a few more cows and I'm anxious to see my Pa and Ma."

Mac admitted to himself that he admired Red. It wasn't often that a young man said that he was homesick and to Mac's way of thinking, it earmarked Red as a decent fellow.

"Red, would you consider working here when you come back through this fall?"

"I might just do that, Mr. MacFarland. I know the horses, the country and a lot of the cattle better than I know most people. I won't make you a promise, but I'll keep the idea in mind."

"We'll add another $10 a month if you do come back this fall, Red. You'd be a segundo for the Silver City wagon."

"That sure sounds good, Mr. MacFarland. I hope it works out."

Red drew his pay, saddled up and headed toward Arizona. He had kept in touch with the Lewis clan who ranched near Cloverdale. He had known the families when they lived in Hope because his parents had many close friends among the Lewis families. In fact, Red knew them well enough that he remembered the names of all the Lewis kids.

Like most of the people he knew, the Lewis bunch didn't think twice about moving westward as the country around Hope filled up with people, barbed wire fences and sheep. The big outfits that ran sheep were crowding out the ranchers who had settled around Hope.

Red had written to the Nora Lewis, a woman he'd grown up calling "Aunt Nora," to tell her that he'd be in their neck of the woods on May 24. He hoped he could stay a day or two and get reacquainted with them on his way to Arizona.

When Red rode into the Lewis ranch, he noticed a lot of activity.

What the heck is going on? Somebody must have died or got married.

He tied his horse to the hitching rail, took his war bag off the back of his saddle and loosened the cinch. Before he could turn around, he was surrounded by a chattering, laughing hoard of Lewis kids. When Red could get a word in, he asked, "Hey, you kids, what's going on around here?"

Blain, older and larger than most of the kids surrounding Red, proudly announced, "We're having a big dance and barbeque for you tonight. Everybody in the country is here. It's gonna be a big blow-out."

"Well I'll be dogged," Red mumbled as he broke away from the children and headed for the house.

Aunt Nora greeted him at the door with a enthusiastic hug. "Come on in, Red," she invited, "you know most of these folks." She motioned to a room full of women. "We're having a little get-together tonight. Hope you shined your boots."

"No, ma'am," Red laughed, "but it looks like I might get my belt buckle polished tonight seeing as how all these purty women are just standing around waiting to dance with me."

The women laughed and several promised him dances.

Red backed out the door and headed for a group of men he'd spotted in the back yard. They were standing around the barbeque pit. The clan patriarch, called Bee, for the letter B, Lewis so as not to confuse him with the other "Blains" named after him, stepped forward to greet Red and shake his hand.

"Unsaddle your horse, Red, and throw your war bag in the bunk house, then get back here. We just opened a new jar of corn squeezings. If you get a hurry on, we might just save you a snort or two."

Red led his horse to the corral. Man, it's almost like being home with ma and pa.

The tables were loaded with angel food cake, pecan pies, peach cobbler, ginger bread and a dazzling array of other deserts.

Speaking to no one in particular, Red gazed at sweet and savory bounty and said, "Holy cow, I think I died and went to heaven. Hey, boys, I'm going to stand downwind of these tables and just soak up the goodness."

Amidst the laughter that followed his declaration, someone said, "Well, Red, don't stand down there and soak too long or you'll find that we've eaten all the food."

The laughter and joshing continued. The wives exclaimed over this pie and that potato salad. Bee Lewis protested with good humor as the other ranchers accused him of butchering anyone's beef but his own for this barbeque.

"Is that so?" he shouted. "Well, you come on over here and I'll show you the hide with my brand on the outside and the inside." The ranchers hooted and slapped Bee on the back.

The beef was pronounced done and the men took it out of the barbeque pit, sliced it on a massive, oak cutting block and loaded serving plates with mountains of fragrant, perfectly cooked beef. That signaled the official start of the meal.

Men, women and children loaded their plates and sought places at the tables to eat. A big, black coffee pot bubbled on some coals taken from the barbeque pit. Ranchers filled cups with steaming coffee to wash down a delicious meal.

The noisy children ate ravenously at a separate table. They squabbled and jostled and thoroughly enjoyed the whole experience.

Young, single women, dressed to kill, batted their eyelashes at the slicked-up, sunburned cowboys.

The cowboys, in turn, were like pigs in mud – wallowing in all the female attention. Their boots were polished, Levis creased and most of them sported short new haircuts that revealed tender white skin that hair had hidden from the light of day for a long time.

Several of the families at the party had traveled forty miles or more to get there. They had come in wagons and buggies with their bed rolls in the back so they could bed the kids down before the dancing started.

Many of the younger partygoers arrived on horseback – the girls with carefully wrapped party dresses secured behind the cantle.

This party was a big occasion for the ranch families. It was a chance to see neighbors and catch up on news. Most of the time, ranchers were so busy with the cattle, that visiting came in a distant second.

Red noticed that when Margaret and her puny suitor arrived, they didn't rush over to join the younger set who were holding court. They sat by themselves or visited with the already-married couples.

Margaret looked longingly in Red's direction. When he noticed it, Red became very interested in a pretty brunette from Cloverdale.

When the feasting was done, everyone adjourned to the concrete slab under the oak trees. It had been specially poured for occasions such as this. Young Blain was sprinkling the floor with cornmeal so dancing boots would slide more easily.

Observing the preparations, Red commented to the brunette, "Hooeee, that Lewis clan loves to dance. Most of them are good musicians, too."

"Why, yes, they are. And on top of that, they are excellent horsemen. They have the grace and balance of a rider and an ear for rhythm. That's probably why they are excellent dancers." The brunette looked at Red quizzically. "My name is Mary. I saw you in the kitchen earlier. You're Red, aren't you?"

"Pleased to make your acquaintance, Mary."

The first dancers took to the floor when the fiddlers struck up a tune. It was an old breakdown the musicians had learned from other fiddlers in the Sacramento Mountains in New Mexico while they lived in Hope.

"They're playing, 'Dance with Me Charlie,'" Red observed, "so how about dancing with me, Mary?"

Mary acquiesced and they joined the dancers. Soon the floor was crowded – everybody liked this song.

The sunset faded and an enormous, full moon crested over the mountains east of the ranch. The new, green leaves on the old trees that surrounded the platform rustled and sighed in a soft, gentle breeze.

I don't think heaven could beat a night like this, Red thought.

During the dance, the Lewis men went though the crowd selling raffle tickets for a horse. The person who had the lucky number drawn out of a ten-gallon hat at midnight would be the new owner of a coveted Lewis-raised horse. Everybody knew they raised the very best horses in the area.

Red had three silver dollars in his pocket. Since he had ridden away from his grandpa in Sonora with three dollars in his pocket – and he still felt lucky his drunken grandfather hadn't shot him in the back – three dollars were his rabbit's foot. Red just didn't feel right if he didn't have three dollars jingling in his pocket, but he happily gave them up to buy three tickets. He stuffed the tickets in his pocket and grabbed a curvaceous redhead and led her to the floor. They danced "Put Your Little Foot," or The Varsovienne, as the women liked to call it.

Red danced every dance and between sets he had a couple quick snorts of corn liquor. He was feeling no pain.

At midnight, the crowd grew quiet. Bee walked across the dance floor and stepped up on the platform where the fiddlers had been playing. He blew a blast from an old Texas hunter's horn.

"Since there's not an honest man or woman present tonight," Bee shouted, "I'm going to ask my neighbor's little daughter, Verna, to draw the winning number. Do you all agree?"

"Yes, yes, yes," the crowd yelled. "Let 'er rip. Draw the number."

Verna, dressed in a homemade, starched pink dress, walked bashfully toward Bee, took his hand, looked up and said, "Mr. Lewis, let's get this over with."

The crowd hooted with laughter. Bee shuffled the numbers in the hat, held it above his head, shuffled again and then squatted down in front of Verna.

"Alright Verna, let's find out who's going to win that good horse."

Bee took the number from Verna and announced in a loud voice. "Our winner is number 13."

Red looked at his numbers and then looked again. For a second he was speechless. The crowd waited.

"Well, I'll be danged," Red announced. "I've got number thirteen. I guess you made them all thirteen so you could have a laugh."

Red walked across the stage and presented his slip to Bee.

"It's fixed," an old cowman yelled. "Bee gives a big celebration for Ol' Red and he wins the prize."

"I demand a redraw," someone hollered.

"You really hornswaggled us, Bee. I wanted that horse. Red don't need but one nohow."

Someone led the horse up to the edge of the dance floor. He was a big, three-year-old, bay, streaked-faced gelding. He showed a lot of breeding.

Red looked at the horse and said, "Oh man, I just fell in love."

Bee handed the lead rope to Red and the whole crowd whooped, yelled and whistled. They all coveted the horse, but everybody liked Red and they were glad for him. For his part, Red couldn't believe his luck. He sure could use an extra horse for his trip to Arizona.

Red shook Bee's hand, thanked him and turned to the crowd. "My ma always taught me to be honest when it was handy. It was sure handy tonight. When I come back through here this fall, I promise you that the purtiest gal in Arizona will be sitting on this good, bay horse."

The celebration lasted until sun-up.

Chapter Fifteen

Nooning on the Cherry Cows

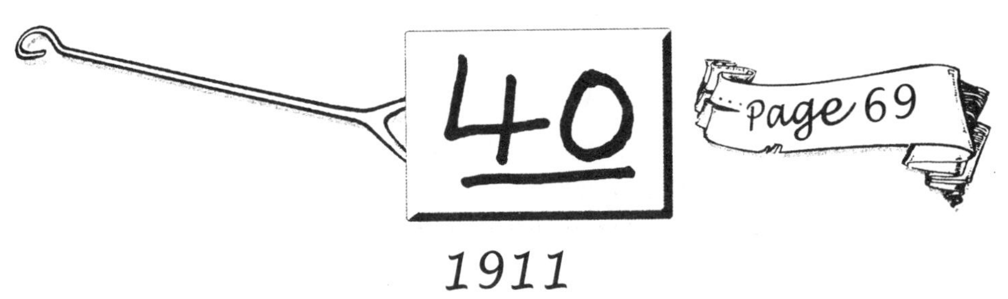

1911

A week later, Red arrived at his destination which was called the Nooning Camp. It belonged to the CCCs and was the furthermost camp on the west side of the ranch. It was near the Dragoons where Cochise had holed up before he was captured by Oliver Howard in 1872. Red was sure glad to see something instead of the tumbleweed flats. He had ridden through them for days on end between Cloverdale, San Simon, Bowie and Wilcox.

Man, oh man, Red thought, what a bunch of wasted country. The good Lord must have been purty mad at someone when he made this part of Arizona. Either that or he was preparing them for hell.

It wasn't even June and the temperature was already over 100°. Who would live in a place like this? He mused. But, I seen quite a lot of cattle and they weren't in bad shape. I figure the winters here must be pretty mild. Some old boy told me that yucca stalks are good cow feed. It looks the cows had plenty of them this spring.

It was evening when he rode into camp. The cook was ringing the triangle. Red had timed it just right to get there at supper time.

Jim was coming up from feeding the horses at the corrals when he saw Red riding in. He'd have known him a mile off. No one sat a horse like Red did.

As he hurried to meet Jim, Red realized how homesick he'd been for family. The brothers embraced.

They led Red's horses to the barn where they unpacked and unsaddled them. From there, they headed to the cook shack. They fell in line with a dozen other cowboys.

"Fellows, I want you all to meet my brother, Red," Jim proudly announced to the hands. "Cookie, this here's my brother Red," he continued as they held out their plates to the grizzled chef for a generous helping of meat and potatoes.

Red fell into the steak and gravy like it was the last meal he'd have before the hanging.

The cowboys teased the cook and carped, hoping to get a rise out of him.

Red knew how much the hands enjoyed tormenting the cook, so he made a special point to speak directly to the cook and tell him that the meal was good and that he appreciated it.

The other hands hit the hay as soon as they had eaten, but Red and Jim walked over to an old log. The young men sat on the ground with their backs braced against it.

"All right," Jim commanded, "we've got lots of news to get caught up on. Now, tell me…"

They talked long into the night. Finally, when they were so tired they couldn't say another word, they rolled out Red's bedroll and soogan on the bunkhouse floor. The two cowpokes fell asleep happily knowing they were finally together.

The wagon boss hired Red the next morning and cut out six horses from the remuda for him. Red turned his two horses into a little pasture where they could rest up from the long trip from the Diamond As. He would use them when needed for the roundup and to keep them tuned up if a roping came along.

They stayed busy branding the late calves and doctoring screw worms that were especially bad that summer. Red liked the job, enjoyed being with Jim and seeing new country.

The CCCs ran from the Dragoons through the Sulphur Springs Valley to the Chiricahua Mountains. It was prime cattle country and the Boices, who owned it, were good people to work for.

June passed mighty fast. They didn't leave the camp but a time or two when they rode over to Dragoon to get some necessary items like chewing tobacco and some clean socks.

On the last excursion to town before the Fourth of July holiday, they purchased a can of Shinola boot polish and some Bay Rum so they'd smell good to the gals at the dance and rodeo at Light.

Red and Jim were both planning to enter the steer and calf roping and Red in the saddle bronc riding. There would be a big dance the night of the Fourth and the cowboys looked forward to the dance more than competing in the rodeo. They liked to hold those pretty gals at the dance and besides, they roped and rode every day. It was no big deal except for the keen competition to match their skills against their buddies' and who would win in the the bronc riding – man or beast. The prize money was slim pickings because this show was mostly local cowhands and ranchers.

There was a whole lot of bragging going on. Red did his share, riding and roping was as natural as walking, he'd done it all of his life.

Win, lose or draw, what the hell, I'll be having a good time.

Because the celebration was about forty miles from the Nooning, they left the day before the Fourth. The events would start early the next morning. They wanted to rest their horses as much as possible and, as long as they had a few days off, they didn't want to miss a thing.

They stopped at the Mercantile in Pearce, bought a few pints of white lightning at the bar and a couple of packages of Juicy Fruit gum to kill the whiskey odor. It was not courteous to ask a gal to dance smelling like you had just had a snort.

Tied behind their saddles were their war bags with their dancing clothes – a clean pair of Levis and a white shirt. When they left the cow camp, their party clothes, ironed and creased by the cook for a price were ready to go, but when the shindig started the next night it would take quite a few sets to dance the wrinkles out.

They arrived at their destination just at dusk. They didn't want to push their horses. They wanted them fresh the next day for the rodeo. They fed and watered their horses and turned them in with the community herd in the arena. Red and Jim hoped they all got along so there would be no sore-backed roping horses the next day. The accommodations for the horses were a long way from being first class.

Some of the squatters wives from the Kansas Settlement had the food concession. These families, who had just arrived in the last few years to homestead, were having a hard time making ends meet. They'd make a few dollars this way. The nearest town was several miles away and didn't have a café anyhow.

The women who would attempt to feed the crowd had rolled a chuck wagon under a big cottonwood tree. The shade would be welcome the next day. It was here they unpacked the roasts, beans, homemade light bread, potato salad and cold slaw they'd brought from home. On the dessert table were fruit cobblers cooked in a Dutch oven and still hot. The cowboys were generous with the thick cream they poured on the dessert and added to their coffee. This was the real stuff, unlike the evaporated milk they usually had. These tables were the most popular location on the Pampas. Cowboys liked sweets and were always behind on them.

After much visiting, the cowboys stretched out on their saddle blankets using their saddles for pillows. The night was warm and they needed no covers.

They went to sleep with great anticipation, for tomorrow would be a great day for the cowboys who had ridden so far and waited so long.

Nell & Ola

Chapter Sixteen

Her Name is Nell

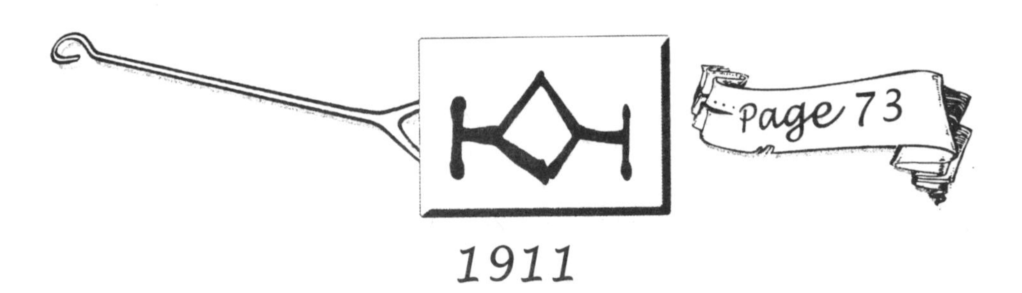

1911

Red and Jim had always been taught to take care of their horses before taking care of themselves. They caught them out of the community corral where all the horses had spent the night.

They put halters on the two they planned to compete on that day and led them out to a little grassy draw where they could graze. Jim talked one of the ranchers who lived at Pearce out of a couple of feeds of oats. He took them back and hung a gunny sack morral on each horse's head. The oats were a treat because they were seldom grained during the summer months. After the rains started, the new grass was sufficient for a horse that was only ridden every fourth or fifth day. A horse grazed every day but the day he was on duty.

After the horses finished their oats, Red hobbled them and left them grazing in the draw while he and Jim went to the water trough and washed up. They shaved in cold water, trying to see how the job was going in a little cracked mirror lodged in the fork of a mesquite limb.

They blew another four bits on a big breakfast at the chuck wagon where they had eaten the night before. They looked like a million dollars and felt like luck was with them as they went over to the entry table to pay their fees.

"It's not the money we're riding and roping for Jim. It's the exposure. If I win one of these events, I can dance with every gal on Turkey Creek tonight," Red explained, as they walked over to shoot the breeze with the other CCC hands.

The competition grew with the arrival of more and more cowboys. Red wondered who shook them all out of the brush. At this rate, the roping events would last all day. He was in hopes he could arrange a match roping or two. Perhaps he could beat the competition with the best time on three calves and win $50.

Red still thought the competition was more important than the money they vied for. That's what made it so attractive to him. He knew he was good, but, he'd seen some mighty fast horses and mighty good ropers come out of the sticks.

The Howell brothers cut a wide swath. They took most of the pots in the collective ropings and all of the matched ones.

Red drew a big, roan gelding in the saddle bronc riding event and won, but by a very slim margin.

Damn, he thought, these ol' Arizona boys sure know how to mark a bronc. I figure I'll just stick to roping while I'm in Arizona. I'll quit while I'm ahead – that's my policy – don't push your luck.

The Boice family owned all this country. That night they put on a big barbeque. Later the fiddlers started tuning up. Bales of hay for seats were placed around the spacious concrete slab used for dancing. Everyone was keyed for action.

After Red and Jim tended to their horses, they washed off as good as they could at the horse trough, put on their white shirts and clean Levis, knocked the dust and cow manure off their boots and waded in.

Red let his eyes drift over the crowd. "Man, there are sure lots of pretty gals here tonight."

One tall, thin girl in a red dress made him look at twice. He thought he'd never seen anything as pretty. She had coal black hair all fancied up and green eyes. He sure hoped she wasn't married.

The next time he looked that way there were half a dozen cowboys standing around her asking for a dance.

So, she is single. That's good news, Red thought.

He couldn't help remembering the lady in red he'd met up with in Roswell while he was working for the Turkey Tracks.

"Good Lord," he said to Jim, "Remember, I told you about when cousin Will and I went to Roswell?"

"Yeah Red," Jim answered, "what brought that up?"

"That tall gal in the red dress. You don't think she's one of them?" Red asked.

"She wouldn't be allowed at this dance if she was, Red. This is a family get-together. I just asked old Jack Busenbark here, who she was and he said her pa has a ranch up Turkey Creek. He's trying to court her, but as you can see, he has to stand in line."

"Wonder if he'd introduce us to her? I'd sure be willing to stand in line for a dance." Red said.

"Give it a try Red. If she's raised proper, like Jack says, she wouldn't dance with you without an introduction. I've got other fish to fry, it's up to you, Red, or you can stand there and gawk all night," Jim said as he walked away.

"Jack, who is that tall gal in the red dress that all them cowboys are flirting with? I'd like to be introduced to her and see if she can dance."

"That's Nell and she sure can dance all right Red, and she's probably a better cowboy than half the hands here. She can ride anything and has a lot of cow savvy. She teaches school at Dos Cabezes. Her folks have a good ranch up Turkey Creek. The gal standing next to her is her sister, Ola. She's married to an ol' boy named Tom Price. They have a ranch just a few miles from here. Nell's probably staying with them over the Fourth. I'm going to ask if I can see her home."

"You'd better get your name in the pot. It looks like she might have a whole roundup crew to escort her home," Red observed.

The dancing had begun. Everyone was in a holiday mood. Red met and danced with several of the girls. He was dancing with a pretty redhead named Maude Hunt to whom he had just been introduced and ventured to ask. "Do you know that tall gal in the red dress?

"My goodness sake," Maude said. "She's my best friend. They live up Turkey Creek from my dad's place. We visit when we can. She rides a lot with her papa and teaches school at Dos Cabezas in the winter after the cattle are shipped. She's sure a good hand."

This made Red want to meet her even more. He liked a woman who was a hand with a horse. He didn't take to these city fillies who were afraid to get their hair mussed up.

When that set was finished, Maude took him over where Nell and some other girls were sitting, taking a break, after a fast paced dance they called the Chicken Scratch.

"Nell, this is Red Howell. Red, Miss Choate."

Red looked into Nell's green eyes and muttered, "Glad to meet you, ma'am. I guess you wouldn't dance with me, would you?"

"I'll dance with you Mr. Howell if you won't call me "ma'am.' Are you from Texas or what?" she asked.

"I guess you'd call me a Texan – nothin' wrong with a Texan that another couple of months in Arizona won't cure."

Nell was very direct. "You work for the Three Cs? Most Texans manage to drift out here sooner or later."

"I'm just here for a couple more months with my brother, Jim. We both work for the Cherry Cows. We're camped over at the Nooning now. I haven't seen the rest of the ranch, but we'll be moving over here soon, I hear."

About six sets later, it was Red's turn.

I like to hold a tall woman – don't have to stoop to hear what she's saying. Boy, can she dance. Tall and willowy. Keeps perfect time to the music. She lets me lead.

He fell in love that night.

Later, after several dances with her, he heard her sister say, "Nell, it's time to go home. It's past midnight."

"Oh, Ola, we can't go now. The dance will last a couple more hours. Please let's stay a while longer," Nell pleaded.

"Tom has been rarin' to go for an hour, Nell. We'll get your horse while you go behind the little brush arbor and change into your riding skirt."

The ladies-only brush-arbor had been built for events like this. Many of the folks came from miles away and the girls needed privacy to change into their Sunday best and out of their riding skirts or whatever they wore to get to the dance.

Red approached Nell's sister. "Mrs. Price, if Miss Choate will permit me, I'd sure like to see her home," Red stated.

He was nearby and had heard the conversation between the sisters.

"Why Mr. Howell, we hardly know you. In fact, the Hunts – Maude and her brother – will be with us, so there's no need for you to go, too. You'd just have to come back here, and from the looks of things, you're having a great time," Ola observed. "We wouldn't like to put you out."

"Well, how am I going to get to know you all if I'm not allowed to ride along?" Red was sorely disappointed and a little angry at being brought up on the carpet by Nell's sister.

"Maybe when you all come back to Headquarters, we'll have a little get-together at my dad's ranch and you and Jim and some of the other boys can come over. We'll ask some of the young folks from the Kansas Settlement. It isn't too far from Turkey Creek where we live."

Nell paid close attention to the conversation. She liked that red-headed drifter from New Mexico and she wanted to see him again before he went back to the Diamond As. Earlier that evening, he had told her his plans for the summer.

Red tuned to Nell. "Miss Choate, I won't forget that invitation and, if by chance I meet your folks when we get over here on this side of the ranch, I'll ask if I can call on you." Red made a courtly bow, mostly in jest.

"Our folks are from Texas," Ola told him when Nell excused herself to go change. "They came from San Saba County. Only been here since the '80s."

"San Saba ain't too far from Kerrville, but I've never been there." Red explained. "I left Texas when I was fifteen and haven't been back, so I don't know much about that country."

"You sure learned to rope somewhere between Kerrville and Light," Ola's husband, Tom, said as he walked up leading their three horses.

"I had plenty of competition today," Red stated, "and after the near miss for first on that big roan, I'm giving up riding broncs until I get back to New Mexico. You ol' Arizona boys are too good for me."

Tom laughed. "They've had that horse in the string for several years. This is the first time he's ever been rode. It looked like they rigged the drawing. They do that to outsiders here."

"I'll be damned," Red exclaimed. Excuse me ma'am." he said to Ola. "I had a ride, that's for sure. Glad they rigged the draw. I'll know better next time. How long does it take a guy to get over being an outsider?"

"It ain't easy," Tom replied, "you almost have to be born here, like we all were. You watch them next time. They're going to get somebody hurt with them ol' outlaws that know all the tricks."

"I've already told Jim that I'm giving up the bronc riding if there's another rodeo while I'm here. I sure don't want to get crippled up. I'm just almost 25 – I still gotta lot of living to do." he said looking pointedly at Nell who had just returned. She looked just as pretty in the divided skirt as she had in the red dress.

Red had to pull his eyes away from her.

Boy, she's knocked me for a loop. She's just the kind of a gal I've been looking for. Pretty as a speckled pup and she has cow-sense. You couldn't beat that combination if you tried.

As the left, Red stood and watched them ride out of the circle of lantern light into the moonlit darkness of the night.

Dang, I feel like an ol' calf cut off from the herd by a barb-wire fence. They sure let me know that I don't belong in the same pasture with them. Nell called me a Texas drifter and I guess that's what I am. One thing about it, at least I'm not waiting around for my folks to die so I can inherit the ranch like these rich Arizona kids.

He turned and went back to the dance platform but all the fun had gone out of the Fourth of July celebration. It had just ridden off into the moonlight.

Chapter Seventeen

Thirty-miles-an-hour?

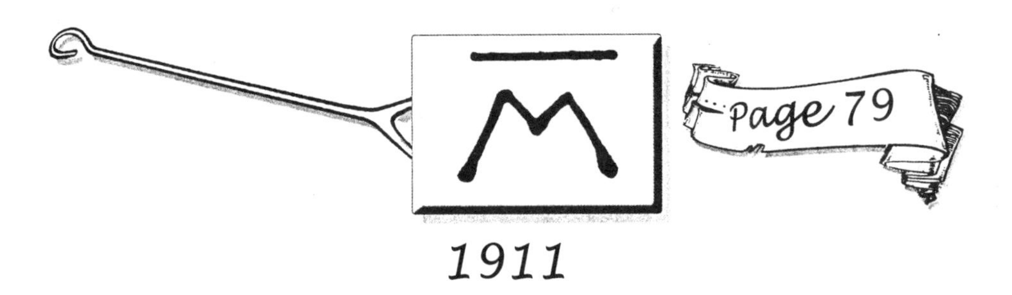

1911

Red and Jim were in the half of the crew that the wagon boss sent from the Nooning Camp to Headquarters. Two weeks had passed since the Fourth of July celebration in Light.

"I'm ready to go," Red commented as they rode. "I'm ready to see some new country at that end of the ranch."

"Yep, me too," Jim replied.

"This sure is good cow country, Red observed. "How big is this ranch anyway?"

"It goes from the Dragoon Mountains," Jim pointed west to a ragged range of blue mountains, "to the flats they call Sulphur Springs Valley and then up into the foothills of the Chiricahua Mountains."

"Well, Jim, I've worked for quite a few outfits and I'd have to say that this is as close to a perfect cow operation as I've ever seen."

Red wasn't disappointed with his new location. Every day was an adventure in a countryside steeped in the Southwestern history that he grown to love.

"You know," Red told Jim as they lounged on their bunks after the evening meal, "Tombstone is just about dead, but I can still see all those gunfighters and miners drinking, gambling and fighting.

"We were running some cows," he continued, "up by an old place the men called Galeyville. The told me the Wild Bunch holed-up there. Later, Slim pointed out an oak tree where Johnny Ringo was found dead."

"I know that place," Jim said. "Isn't it there where those two, little roads fork about half way between Headquarters and Turkey Creek?"

"Yes sir, that's it. The other day a couple fellows showed me where the Apaches had raided and killed several families."

"I can't help but wish I had lived back in the Outlaw Days."

"What would you have done? Robbed banks and stagecoaches?"

"No, I'd like to have been on the other side of the deal. I would have been a lawman, chasing those bad *hombres* down. I guess I'd have to help hang them at the end of the day. I can't say I like that idea too much. That might be a shade too Western for me."

Jim grinned, punched his arm and said, "Well, brother, you can roll over and dream about tracking down all those lawbreakers."

One day the mail bag contained a letter addressed to:

The Howell Brothers
c/o CCC Cattle Company
Willcox Star Route
Willcox, Arizona

Red knew, as he slit the envelope open with his pocket knife, that the letter contained the invitation to a party at Turkey Creek Ranch. After reading the note, Red peered intently at the signature: Nell Choate. He turned it this way and that as if hoping to find a secret message in the signature.

"By golly," he muttered, "I almost gave up on this deal."

"Jim," Red shouted, "come here and listen to this."

"You are invited to a farewell party for Hill Hunt. Hill will be leaving Turkey Creek to take a new job at San Simon."

Jim slapped his dusty hat against his leg. "Dang it, Red, I'll sure be glad to do something other than chasing cows and eatin' dust. All we do from sunup to sundown is build fence, shoe horses or brand and move cattle. We haven't been to town since they moved us over here."

"Who's a courtin' you two?" Mr. Boice, their boss had noticed how excited the brothers were as they read their mail.

"It's not that, Mr. Boice. It's a party at the Choate ranch for a fellow named Hill Hunt who's taking a new job over at San Simon. They invited Jim and me. Say, do you think we can have that day off? I've heard it's quite a ride over there."

Mr. Boice laughed. "Of course you and Jim can have the day off – two, if you want to stay over."

Mr. Boice peered more closely at the young cowhands. "You both need to get your red curls cut off. You're wooly. I'm going to Willcox tomorrow in my Model T Ford. Do you boys want to ride in with me and get a hair cut?"

Red glanced over at Jim who nodded his head. "Yes sir, we'd appreciate that. I never rode in a motor car before, but I'd sure like to give it a try."

Mr. Boice grinned. "You boys be ready at 4:30 A.M.. It takes a while to get there even in the automobile. If the thing gives out on us, you two big fellows can push."

"Hot damn," Red exclaimed. "I'm so excited that I don't think I'll be able to get a wink of sleep tonight."

Jim laughed. "I know just how you feel."

Willcox was forty miles from the ranch and the road was a deeply rutted wagon track. Mr. Boice, who was just learning how to drive his new contraption, kept the speed at around twenty-miles-per-hour regardless of the condition of the road. Red and Jim held onto their hats with one hand and the seat with the other as the open vehicle bucked and bounced down the road. Red was amazed to see fence posts going by so quickly and thought: *I never would have believed that a person could travel so fast.*

Folks say that automobiles are just a passing fad, but if they do stick around, I want one for myself, Red thought as the wind whistled in his ears. *Man, wouldn't I be in high cotton then?*

As they arrived in Willcox, Red could see that the stores and banks were just starting to open.

Mr. Boice took the Model T to a little gas station garage. When the mechanic came over, Boice said, "Say, would you tune up the motor? It backfired and stuttered all the way over here. It has a seven-gallon gas tank. Please top it off. We have some business to take care of. We'll be back about 2:00 to pick it up."

The mechanic gave Mr. Boice a silent salute and the three men piled out of the vehicle.

"Why look at that," Red pointed at a sign. "Gas is just ten-cents a gallon. If we used up the whole tank, that means it just cost us seventy-cents to come this far. That's cheaper than horse feed."

Mr. Boice chuckled. "Yes, if you forget the initial cost. Do you know how many steers it took to buy this piece of machinery?"

"Damned if I know. Let's see. A good steer is worth about $20, right? Red asked.

"Yep," Mr. Boice replied, "and it took twenty-head of good steers to buy this motor car. I guess it was worth it. Just think about it: I could go all the way from the ranch to Tucson in only two days if there weren't any problems."

Later, while he was getting his hair cut by a real barber, Red mulled over his life. *Here I am getting my first, paid-for hair cut after traveling across the country in a motor car. By golly, I'm sure comin' up in the world. Life here in Arizona is purely a pleasure.*

Red dozed off in the barber chair, surrounded by sweet smells and idle conversation.

The barber was gently tugging his shoulder. "For only a dime more, I can put some Brilliantine on your hair." The barber looked expectantly at Red and Jim. In spite of the fact that he didn't know what Brilliantine was, he took his cue from Jim's scowl and said confidently, "No thanks, we won't be needing Brilliantine today."

As they left the barber shop and headed for the mercantile, Jim confided, "Red, I don't know what that Brilliantine stuff is, but I figured we didn't need to spend any more money or take any chances."

It was almost dark when they got back to the ranch. Mr. Boice explained that the Model T wasn't equipped with running lights for night driving, so it was lap-and-tap to get home while there was still enough light to see.

The boys stowed their purchases on their bunks and headed to the cook shack for some supper. The old, black cook was madder than hell because the rest of the crew had finished eating an hour earlier and there weren't any leftovers.

"Son-of-a-gun, I done finished cooking for the day and now you all want me to cook again."

"Hey, Cookie," Red tried to placate him, "I'll stir us up something. You go on to bed. I'll clean everything up."

"Hell no. I'm not letting some dumb cowboy in my kitchen to mess everything up. I'll throw something together for you. A cold biscuit and some lick ought to do it."

"That's fine with us, but let me ask you something." Red pulled a half pint of whiskey from his hip pocket and held it up. "What would this buy us?"

The grizzled cook grabbed the bottled, uncorked it with his teeth, spit the cork halfway across the room and took a long pull on the bottle.

"Damn, that's good stuff. It'll buy you the best steak on that carcass hanging in the cold room."

"Don't bother about biscuits, Cookie." Jim grinned and handed the cook a bag. When he opened the bag, the sweet smell of a fresh loaf of bread wafted into the room.

"I done died and gone to heaven. Store-bought bread. You two sit down and I'll get the coffee pot on. The cook contentedly took another swig from the flask.

Red chuckled and said, "He'll be cranky as hell in the morning when the glow wears off."

Tired and happy, Jim and Red left the cook shack. "That," Red proclaimed, "was the best meal we've had since we've been here. We'll have to lay in a supply of whiskey for him. Who knows, we might even get a peach cobbler some day.

It was still four days until the party and Red was getting more antsy as each day passed. Jim knew things were bad when he saw his brother throw a Red Howell fit when one of the green hands left a gate open and let a bunch of cattle out of the pasture they'd just worked. It took half-a-day to get the cows back through the gate.

Red had just about recovered from that indignity when his horse threw a shoe in some rocky country. Red had to let the other cowboys do the rest of the gathering while he ate dust behind the herd, trying hard not to cripple his horse.

"Jim, I'll tell you, Saturday just can't get here quick enough."

Jim agreed with that. "I'll just be glad to get the whole thing over with so I don't have to put up with any more of your ranting and raving."

Jim didn't carry on and even that aggravated Red. Jim calmly waited for the party with pleasant anticipation and he tried to stay as far away from Red as he could.

On the day of the party, Jim and Red arrived at 4:00, just as the invitation had specified.

"It's a pleasure to meet you, Mr. and Mrs. Choate," Red replied when he was introduced to Nell's parents.

They seem like nice people, Red thought. My goodness, her mother is a slim, little thing. She sure has pretty eyes – black and sparkling. She is hospitable. I feel like I've known her forever.

Her father, Red observed, is a big man. Clean shaven. They introduced him as Gabriel Choate the third.

Fancy name. He must be 6'5" but he isn't hunched over like some tall men. No slouching for him. Why, he's as straight as an arrow and he walks like a man who spends a whole lot of time in the saddle.

Jim commented, as the Choates walked away, "I've heard about him. They say he's as strong as a bear. One cowboy told me that he saw old man Choate lift a 55-gallon barrel full of water off the ground and put it in the bed of a wagon."

"That's quite a feat," Red replied. "After meeting him, I'd have to say it's possible he did that."

Nell had two brothers. Bill was a few years younger than she. He was handsome and he knew it. There was already a whole covey of girls there and he was entertaining them royally.

Miles Rutherford Choate, Nell's younger brother, was eleven-years-old. He was a typical little brother who began teasing Red as soon as soon as he stepped off his horse near the barn.

"Say, are you Red? You must be quite a catch. My sister spent all morning getting dolled up. Are you going to dress like that for the party? What kind of horse are you riding? Is that the saddle you won at Light?"

The boy peppered Red with a nonstop torrent of questions and comments. Red smiled, ruffled the boy's hair and said, "Son, I need to say howdy to the other folks, but come by later and we'll have a man-to-man talk."

The boy stuck out his hand and said, "Folks call me Poke. My real name is Miles Rutherford but my daddy said that when I was real young I had a long, sick spell. One of my uncles started calling me 'Poco Malo.' That means something like 'a little sick' in the Mexican language. Pretty soon, everybody was calling me 'Poke.'"

"Well, I'm mighty please to meet you, Poke." Red shook the boy's small hand in his huge paw.

"Folks call me 'Red.' I don't rightly know why."

Poke chuckled appreciatively at the joke and replied, "Red, I'll see you later."

The boy ran off and Red knew Poke must be popular in this part of the country.

By the time all the guests had arrived, the ranch yard and corrals were filled with wagons, buggies, horses and people.

The younger guests congregated on the porch and in the front yard. The excited talk and laughter filled the yard with energy and promised a successful party.

The women bustled about, setting up a picnic under a huge pecan tree in the front yard. Red hauled watermelons to help Mrs. Choate.

"How do you like my tree? I brought this tree with me from Texas."

Red raised an eyebrow as he studied the enormous tree.

Mrs. Choate laughed. "It was just a little sapling that I tucked away in the wagon when we came here in the late '80s."

"Well, Mrs. Choate, I'd have to say that your tree certainly seems to be happy in its new home."

The supper ended with homemade ice cream and fresh peaches. As Red savored every cool, sweet, delicious spoonful, Poke, sitting at his elbow, gave a running commentary.

"My daddy went to Douglas yesterday. We have a big orchard that we water from a spring. Daddy sells the extra fruit that mama doesn't can to the miners. Daddy says those poor miners can't get enough of that fresh fruit.

"Daddy bought a 300-pound block of ice yesterday." Poke gestured with his arms to show the size of this mountain of ice. "Daddy got back to the ranch just before you and your brother rode in."

"A couple of the hands unloaded that block of ice and covered it with tarps. Do you know how much ice was left?"

Red shook his head.

"200-pounds of that ice melted. Daddy said there was about 100-pounds left. Mama said that was plenty for a couple of freezers of ice cream."

"Did you ever see them make ice cream?" Poke continued on without giving Red a chance to reply. "You have to crank the freezers by hand. The fellow who was doing the cranking gets to choose a girl to sit on the freezer to keep it from tipping over. Isn't that silly? A guy would weigh more. Why didn't the guys sit on the freezers?

Poke gave Red a sly, sideways glance. "Nell sat on one freezer or the other most of the time."

As darkness fell, the party moved inside. The men rolled up the rugs and moved back the furniture with a sureness born of having done this traditional procedure at many ranch parties.

To get their courage up for dancing, the boys wandered off to the corrals to roll and smoke a Bull Durham cigarette and have a nip from the flask being passed around.

Meanwhile, the girls quickly helped Mrs. Choate clean up the kitchen so they could get down to the serious business of getting ready for the dance. They assembled in Nell's upstairs bedroom. The warm air in the small, high-ceilinged room was redolent with the smell of young bodies and inexpensive perfume. The girls chattered like a flock of colorful, exotic birds as they primped, patted and powdered. Some of the more adventurous girls rouged their lips with a blob of wet, red, crepe paper. Then, on some silent signal, the girls flowed down the stairs in a cloud of giggles, anticipating the first dance.

There were three musicians in the corner with a fiddle, a guitar and a button accordion. The fiddler struck the first chord.

During the lively party, Nell took an occasional break from the dance floor to play the piano in accompaniment of the other musicians. As she played one of her favorite songs, Hill Hunt walked up to the piano.

Hill shuffled his feet, cleared his throat and announced, "You all know I'm leaving tomorrow for a new job at San Simon. I'll be gone for quite a spell, so I'd like to sing Nell a new song I just learned. I figure she won't forget me quite so quick this way."

The crowd clapped and yelled enthusiastically. For her part, Nell was always happy to learn a new song-ballad.

The crowd silenced in anticipation of Hunt's performance. He cleared his throat again and immediately launched into song:

From this valley I tell you I'm going,
I shall miss your sweet face and your smile.
For in leaving, I'll miss all the sunshine
that has brightened my life for a while.
Come and sit by my side if you love me,
Do not hasten to bid me adieu.
Just remember the Sulphur Springs Valley,
And the cowboy who loves you so true.

Hill looked right at Nell. She was more embarrassed than touched by his parody of Red River Valley. After a verse or two, she had picked up the melody and accompanied him.

Red was stunned. In his mind he'd already roped and hogtied Nell and then this clown had jumped in and shot his plans all to hell.

The fun and excitement drained out of the room. The bright colors turned to black-and-white. The party was over for Red.

I don't play second fiddle to nobody. He motioned to Jim. "I'm ready to go," he said.

"Oh for Pete's sake," Jim admonished, "we can't leave just now. It'll make it too plain that you're mad at that fellow for singing to your gal. It just wouldn't look good. You don't have any strings on her, yet."

"Damn it, Jim, you're right. I was sure fixin' to put some strings on her, though." Red breathed deeply a couple of times and felt himself relax. "I doubt that we could find our way back to the Cs in the dark since we don't know this country. Getting lost out there like a couple of city slickers would certainly draw some attention to us. We'd best wait 'til daylight to vamoose."

"We could ride tonight with the bunch from Kansas Settlement part of the way to where the road forks," Jim suggested. We could hobble the horse, take a little nap and head for the ranch from there at sunrise."

Red laughed. "And end up like ol' Johnny Ringo in the morning?

Jim sighed with relief. He was glad Red had cooled down. One thing about a Red Howell fit – it didn't last long.

Twenty-minutes later, the party broke up.

Red and Jim went to Nell. "Thank you, Nell, for inviting us to this fine party," Jim said.

"You are entirely welcome. I'm so glad you came."

She looked pointedly at Red. "Don't let Hill bother you, he's been singing to me since we were in first grade."

She studied his face and she seemed to be looking deep inside him. "Red, I'd sure like to have a letter from you when you get back to the Diamond A." She turned and walked away.

Red's spirits momentarily lifted. Then his mood plummeted. Maybe she's playing me for a sucker. She doesn't seem to be that kind of a gal, but you can never tell about women.

Red spoke to the retreating woman. "You'd better write to me first. I'd sure hate to write you a letter and find out you'd followed Hill Hunt over to San Simon. Just address it to Hachita. They only get two letters a month at that post office.

Chapter Nineteen

The Doggone Flying Machine

1911

The roundup was over on the Diamond As. The next chore was to drive the cattle to the shipping location on the Southern Pacific Railroad at Separ.

The cattle, gathered from all the wagons, numbered more that ten-thousand head, perhaps closer to 15,000. The big job was cutting the yearlings, big calves and culls to be shipped, from the cows and small calves. For three full days the wagon bosses and their segundos rode quietly into the herd and brought out a steer or whatever he saw that needed shipping. The rest of the cowboys were holding the cut. It was hard, nerve-wracking work. The big bosses were there on location watching every move.

Red rode his own horse, Domingo, part of the time. It was the B. Lewis horse he'd won that spring at the barbeque. He had spent his spare hours working with him. Now he was a topnotch roping and cutting horse. To Red, he was a working cowhorse, not a show horse. He was quicker than a cat and he could turn on a dime and give you some change. Red felt honored to be asked to cut since he had been a segundo such a short while.

All hands and cooks rejoiced when the separating was over. On those big flats at Separ were thousands of cattle divided now into two herds and held by at least 50 cowboys.

The long train, made up of cattle car after cattle car was waiting on the siding, ready to receive the livestock bound for California. The Diamond A had feed lots and irrigated pastures to feed out the cattle and ready them for the slaughter houses.

With their ropes and prods, a crew had cut off a hundred or so head and with a lot of cussing and yelling, the cowboys were crowding the first car load up the chutes into the cattle cars.

Above the bawling of cattle and the raised voices of the cowboys, there was suddenly a strange noise no one could identify. They looked skyward and there, lo and behold, was the first flying machine most of the cowboys had ever seen.

The plane was flying low, following the railroad track from coast to coast. This was a phenomenon.

The friendly pilot revved up the motor and circled just above the corrals. The strange noise boogered the cattle. The cowboys, looking up toward the circling plane with jaws agape, forgot there ever was a cow.

Both herds merged. The cows and calves got back together and ran for safety. The cowboys, realizing too late that a stampede was on, spurred their horses into the run trying to get in front of the panicking herd.

The flats around Separ were riddled with prairie dog holes, but the cowboys were so hell-bent on turning back the running cattle that they disregarded the threat. Red saw a horse and rider go down right beside him, but he raced on. It didn't enter his mind that the next wreck could be him and Domingo.

The men finally outran the leaders and got the cattle milling. They had gone about three miles from the shipping pens and the fact finally struck them – they would have three or four more days of cutting and the job would be more difficult because the cows were spooky. Any little thing would stampede them again. The horses were rode down and the cowboys were tired and cranky.

Two horses had dog-holed and had to be put down. The riders were lucky, both survived, one with only a broken leg and the other with a head injury. They were loaded into the big bosses' Overland and driven to Deming where there was a semblance of a hospital. They were left there to recover.

The cowboys knew where they had been positioned before the wreck and took their places the next morning.

The night before Mr. MacFarland had doubled the night guard and put the hands on fresh horses. He knew, that even as tired as they all were, they had to be alert.

Red rode two shifts of night guard. He said he was filling in for Tulk who had broken his leg in the stampede. Red felt he owed it to him because he remembered the horror of seeing man and horse go down during the run.

The train had to be rescheduled and it would remain on the siding another four days. This cost the company a pot of cash and the big bosses were not happy with the dumb cowboys who had let a flying machine delay the shipping.

After the last steer was loaded, the brass left for a less primitive way of life in town. The cattle that belonged to each camp were returned to winter quarters by the cowboys. On the way, Red noticed blocks of salt had been placed by the camp flunkies, while the rest of the crew was doing the shipping.

This done, Red rode back to Hachita with several of the other hands who were also drawing their pay. Red was glad to find his brother, Jim, waiting when he reached the headquarters.

The news of the plane and the big spill had already spread around the country and they took a lot of ribbing about the affair. It was worth it to Red. He'd finally seen a flying machine.

Red had asked Mr. MacFarland to keep his accumulated money in the ranch vault and was delighted to find how much he'd saved during the past three years. Now he could buy more cows to stock his little place in the Guadalupes.

Nell's family up on Turkey Creek

Chapter Twenty

Surviving a Blizzard

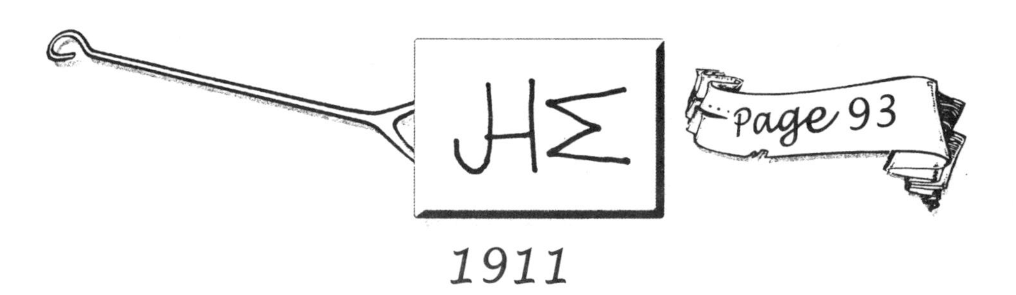

1911

The next day or two, Red and Jim were busy shoeing their horses and getting supplies from the company store for the long trip home. They had Red's extra horse to carry their bed rolls, extra clothes and equipment. The boys were going cross-country and would be camping every night. Their plans were to follow the International Fence between New Mexico and Old Mexico to El Paso, then head northeast by Hueco Tanks, Salt Flat, up Dog Canyon, by Queen and on down to Red's place. They figured this would take eight or nine days without crowding their horses, if all went well.

They were making good time across all that flat country until they hit the Guadalupe Mountains. They were not surprised one morning when a blizzard blew in. The storm had been threatening for a day or two. They had never seen so much snow fall so fast.

"Jim, let's hole up until this storm is over. We don't know the country that good and it's too chancy to try to find the right trail.

"Suits me, Red. These clothes," Jim said gesturing at his worn jeans and shirt, "were fine for Arizona, but I'm freezing. Makes a fellow wonder where his summer wages went."

Red was in the same shape. He was cold, but they had to keep moving. Surely they'd run into a ranch soon.

Night fell and still no sign of civilization. They just happened to ride into a washed out gully with dirt bluffs on each side that broke the wind. The horses, their butts to the wind, were tied to a stubby tree. The brothers tried to stretch a tarp over the bluff for enough protection to start a fire.

"Jim, break some twigs off that stunted tree. Let's try to get a fire going."

They melted snow in the coffee pot, threw in a handful of coffee waited for it to boil.

"Red, make a little small snow ball and throw it in the coffee pot to settle the grounds.

When they finished the coffee and warmed up a little, they filled the morrals with a feed of oats and fed their tired, cold horses. The three horses didn't even flinch when they secured a tarp over them. They took it off periodically and walked and led the horses up and down the little draw where they were camped. Otherwise, they wouldn't have made it, standing all night without activity in the sub-zero cold. Red and Jim had put on dry shirts and Levis on over their slightly damp ones. Their gloves were drying out by the camp fire. They had gotten soaking wet from brushing snow off their chaps.

It was still snowing so hard they could barely see each other across the camp fire.

They wrapped their soogans around themselves and kept the fire going all night.

"I've always had a good sense of direction, Jim. Don't worry," Red said trying to placate his brother who was two years younger.

"Yeah, Red you're good. I've noticed you know the sun comes up in the east and sets in the west." Jim ribbed him, "but with no sun, what the hell do we use to direct us?"

"It'll let up in a while and we'll get our bearings. We know if we start uphill we'll be going deeper into the mountains. Trouble is, we could ride fifty yards from a ranch house and not see it," Red answered, "but we could smell the smoke from the fireplace."

"I couldn't," Jim said, "my nose is froze. I'll probably never smell again."

"That'll be a blessing, especially if it's your feet freezing, too," Red kidded him.

"Hey, it's getting lighter, are you thawed out yet? We got to get our horses moving. They need to stay limber and get some exercise or they'll freeze up and we'll be afoot in this snowstorm.

They shook as much snow as they could off their bed tarps and camp stuff. They would ride wet saddles today for sure.

They rode, hoping they were headed eastward. It all looked the same – just a big country covered with snow. They were riding into the wind and figured it was from the north because of the fury of the storm. They could be traveling in a circle. That evening, just at dark, they rode over a little rise and saw a faint light shining through the snow. With whoops of joy, they spurred their tired horses toward the house.

Ranchers were hospitable people. Red and Jim felt sure they would be asked to spend the night and maybe wait out the storm. Their horses needed rest more than the two, half-frozen men did.

They rode in near the yard and Red yelled "Hello the house." The door flew open and a woman appeared with a rifle in her hands.

"Ma'am, we're the Howell brothers from up around Four Wells. We're lost and froze to death," Red yelled through the storm. "Where's your mister?"

"I'm Olief Lewis and I don't have no damned 'mister.' The nearest town is Orange and that's about 30 miles behind you. Where'd you come from in this storm?"

"We're coming from the Diamond A Ranch at Hachita, trying to get home. We're half froze and our horses are give out. You reckon you'd let us get down and warm a little bit." Red asked.

"Might as well put your horses up first. The barn's that-a-way." She pointed vaguely westward they thought. She shut the door. Red and Jim were left sitting there on their horses.

"Friendly bitch, ain't she?" Red observed.

"Yep," Jim answered, "for a Lewis."

The door swung open and Mrs. Lewis came out all bundled up. The Howell boys got off and let her lead them to the corrals.

They unsaddled, unpacked and rubbed their horses down. Red chopped a hole in the frozen water trough and let their horses drink. Mrs. Lewis had pitched some hay under a little lean-to for them.

"Bring your bedrolls up to the house. You can thaw out by the fireplace."

They brushed the snow off the tarp that covered their bed rolls and took off their spurs and wet chaps, hung them on a nail in the barn and followed Mrs. Lewis back to the house.

They left their bed rolls by the door and stood with their backs to the roaring fire in the big fireplace and knew they'd dodged another bullet. A man could not have survived long in this storm without shelter.

Mrs. Lewis reached into a cabinet and produced a pint of whiskey. Both men drank deeply.

"Might as well start thawing from the inside," Red laughed and handed the bottle back to her and thanked her for saving their lives.

"Did you say we're close to Orange?" Red asked.

"About 30 miles as the crow flies," she replied.

"I'll be damned," Red swore. He added, "Please excuse my language, ma'am. We went plumb wrong. We must have drifted north. I was sure this storm was blowing in from the north, so we thought we were going east toward the Guadalupes."

"You're lucky you saw my light. You'd a rode right by and there's nothing or nobody out there for miles," Mrs. Lewis said as she handed them each a steaming cup of coffee. "You could float a horse on this coffee if it didn't melt the horse first," she chuckled, "but it'll warm your bones."

She offered them milk for their coffee. "I don't keep a milk cow now that my kids is gone," Mrs. Lewis told them several times. "You can buy canned milk. But I'll be danged if you can buy canned eggs. I like to have bacon and eggs every morning"

"You know, boys, this storm blew in from the east. Don't usually get that kind here. It came right on over the Guadalupes and Sacramento mountains. No wonder you were lost."

Red and Jim spent three days with Mrs. Lewis waiting out the storm. The only times they got out of the house was to tend to their horses, fill and relight the kerosene lantern in the chicken coop to keep the hens and eggs from freezing and to heed the call of nature. The men occupied themselves with shoveling narrow paths in the snow to the barn, chicken coop and outhouse. The paths had to be repeatedly cleared as new snow fell.

Red, Jim and Mrs. Lewis whiled away the hours sharing information about all the other members of the Lewis clan. Red told the story of how he had won Domingo at her son's ranch near Cloverdale.

"Mrs. Lewis slapped her leg and laughed, "Well, if that don't beat all. You winning that big, old horse and now you turn up here riding him."

Late in the afternoon of the third day, the storm abated and the wind changed direction, coming out of the south. The warmer wind set the snow to melting rapidly. Red and Jim took advantage of the better weather to chop a fresh supply of wood for Mrs. Lewis. They nailed down the corrugated tin on the barn roof where it had blown off and they did a few chores for her.

They spent one more day with Mrs. Lewis. The snow was melting fast and they wanted to make sure the storm had blown on and there wasn't another following

"Mrs. Lewis," Red asked on the fourth morning, "what can we do to help out?"

"Bless your hearts," she said. "I was widowed back in ought-one and I've run this ranch by myself ever since. You boys had better get back on the road. Here, let me draw you a map so you can find your way back to the trail. There's a shortcut to Dog Canyon and Queen."

"Well, ma'am," Red told her, "we'll head on over to Queen and pick up some supplies. In the meantime, we'll leave what we have to replace what we've used here. We don't want you coming up short in the spring." She was happy to have the flour, coffee and sugar they left and the Howell boys were happy to leave it.

Three days after they left Mrs. David L. Lewis' ranch, the tired and trail-worn brothers arrived at Red's homestead early in the evening. The two-room shack was a welcome sight.

"That old woman sure as shootin' saved our lives," Red said. "She was hospitable and took us in when we needed taking in. For my part, I can tell you that she has a friend for life."

"She can count me as a friend for life, too," Jim agreed.

Jasper. He's Nell's uncle and a good hand

Chapter Twenty-one

The Locket

Christmas, 1911

Though he needed help with the cattle, he let Don and Effie Brown take off a month and go to see their kith and kin in Texas. They had done a good job taking care of the ranch and cattle while Red was at the As and in Arizona. Neighbors helped Red round-up and ship the culls and some yearlings and two-year-olds that Don had missed that fall.

Jim stayed with him a couple of weeks and helped him gather, then the two Howell brothers rode to their parent's ranch for Christmas. It was a big shindig. The Howells never gave a small dinner, the whole clan was invited.

Dovie, Red's oldest sister had married Ole Gossett while Jim and he were off cowboying. Tom, the next in line had a passion for the newfangled automobiles and worked at a garage in Artesia when his pa didn't need him to help with the cattle.

Levi and Ruth, the two youngsters, were in school. They were kids when the boys left and they were happy to reacquaint themselves with their older brothers.

It was a wonderful Christmas with the whole family at home plus cousins, uncles and aunts.

Red had sent Nell a gold locket with her initials etched on the front and a miniature photo of himself inside.

"Oh, crimeny Red, you coulda bought another cow with the money you spent on that locket," Jim exclaimed when Red showed him the gift.

Red was indignant. "Now Jim, it's insurance, so she won't forget me."

Jim laughed and replied, "Red, if I looked like you I'd let her forget. I think you'd make better time with her if she didn't have a reminder of your redhead and freckles wrapped around her neck all the time."

Nell sent Red a beautiful pair of bridle reins she had braided herself. Red kept them for Sundays and the good ropings.

Red planned to ask her to marry him soon and if she accepted, he'd go back to Arizona, get her, and bring her back to New Mexico with him. He could hardly wait.

The Browns came back from Texas and realized that Red didn't need them any longer. They sold him their cattle and bought a small farm at Atoka.

"Red," Don said, "if you do go to Arizona to bring back a bride, we'll stay at the ranch. We can't farm at Atoka in the winter time."

Don helped Red add another room to the homestead shack. Red tried to pretty it up because Nell was used to nice things.

Red looked the place over and commented, "It looks a lot better now that we're finished, but it sure isn't a mansion. In fact, the barn and corrals look better than the house."

Don laughed. "Ranchers are prone to do that. Houses are just somewhere to hang your hat. When you're working cattle, you leave before daylight and get in after dark. All you need is a place to eat and sleep.

"Oh course, the women don't agree. Even if the ranch is at the end of nowhere, they take pride in their homes. Red, you'll find that out soon enough if you marry Nell."

The proposal in his letter to Nell in was brief and to the point:

Dear Friend Nell,

I think we've fooled around long enough. Why don't we get married? I'd sure like to have you over here to see all the little new calves and colts with me. I think it would work out fine, so anytime you're ready, I'll put my horse on the train and go to Douglas. We'll get married over there and ride back here together.

I sure hope you'll say yes. I sure think a lot of you and I think we'd make it just fine together.

You friend,
Lewis (Red) Howell

Her answer was late in arriving. Red was about to give up. He had spent days and days riding deeper into the foot hills, branding the mavericks that had strayed from the surrounding ranches. He generally found them around the water holes where he had packed in salt blocks.

It was a thrill to run onto a wild cow: roping, tripping and tying them down so they couldn't get back on their feet. Then Red built a small fire, took the ring that he carried in his chap's pocket, cut two green branches, crossed them inside the ring, heated it and put his co/ brand on the animal and earmarked it.

Then he tied the cow to a tree with a soft cotton rope around its horns, giving it enough slack to move around, but not enough to get tangled up and injure itself.

After a couple of days, he'd tip the horns with a short saw that he tied behind the saddle. Finally, he with his lariat around the horns, he would dally and lead it to the ranch where he'd keep it penned up a few days with feed and water. Red left a gentle cow in the pen with the maverick until it got used to fences and people.

Gradually, one cow at time, he added to his herd. They were there for the taking if you were cowboy enough to rope them and lead them in. After they left their mothers, they were fair game although, the New Mexico Livestock and Sanitary Board frowned on this practice. The law read that any animal over a year old, weaned from its mother and unbranded belonged to the Territory of New Mexico. The law was not enforced. In the Guadalupe Mountains, if anyone could get a count, the wild unbranded cattle would outnumber those that were branded.

He rode into Lakewood to get the mail and some much-needed groceries. He dreaded going to the post office and finding that his mail box was empty again.

But today, by golly, there was a letter from his sweetie. He was in a hurry to read the letter, but he didn't want to be impolite and not visit with the others who had come in to get their mail. As in all small towns in the West, the post office was the gathering place. It was the social hour when the mail bag came in on the train.

He got on his horse, forgetting the groceries and other things he needed, rode a little way out of town, got off, ground-tied his horse, opened the letter and read:

Dear Friend Lewis,

I decided that since we're going to be married, it would be more polite to call my husband by his real name. Don't you agree?

My teaching contract with the school in Dos Cabezas is for one year and will be complete in May. I think you should come on over here so we can have some kind of a courtship, since we only know each other by mail. I want to be courted.

Let me know when you plan to arrive. They are hiring for the spring works at the Three Cs and that would be near enough for us to see each other quite often.

Your friend,
Nell

Red didn't know whether to throw his ten-gallon hat in the air and yell with joy or throw a Red Howell fit. The letter was so presumptuous – just like she had been expecting him to propose to her.

She sure isn't like any other woman I've ever known. I wish she'd just said she was marrying me because she loved me or she'd be proud to be my wife or something.

Then he remembered that the way he'd proposed to her was like saying, "What are you doing Saturday night?"

They'd make a pair.

Chapter Twenty-two

The Courtship

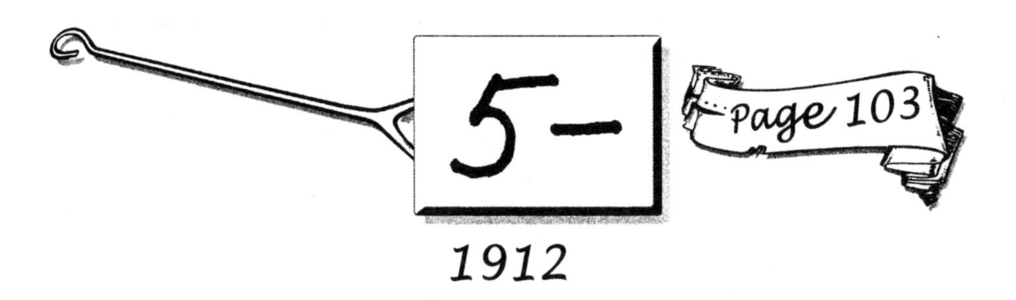

1912

When Red unloaded his horse at the Douglas shipping pens he felt elated as he never felt before. He was within two easy riding-days of the girl with whom he'd spend the rest of his life.

When he arrived at the El Coronado, as the Choate ranch on Turkey Creek was called, they informed him that Nell was at Dos Cabezas, where she taught school, and this meant that it was almost another day's ride to get to see her.

The Choates were hospitable and asked him to spend the night and get an early start in the morning. It wasn't the best night he'd ever spent. After supper, they sat around the huge fireplace and the questioning began.

Red felt that he was standing before the Spanish Inquisition. Mrs. Choate gave the impression that she wasn't exactly in favor of her daughter marrying and moving away off in New Mexico. It might as well be Texas and she let him know that she hated that ugly, dry, windswept country across West Texas and Southern New Mexico.

She had first crossed that country as a bride when she came West with her husband, Gabe, and four of his brothers, their cattle and horses, and her tiny, two-month-old daughter, Ola. They traveled in the only conveyance available at the time; a covered wagon.

It was early spring in 1880s when they left San Saba County, Texas, and the West was still wild. The Apaches were not completely docile and she still remembered the endless miles of salt flats, sage brush and cacti.

Red had a good idea of what she'd say when she saw his little, unpainted claim shack at Four Wells, but he figured he'd done pretty good in his twenty-six years. Probably better than most dollar-a-day cowboys.

The Three Cs were pleased to have him back for the spring works. When Red told them why he was back in Arizona, they wanted him to take one of the permanent camps.

He explained that he had a little outfit in New Mexico and planned to return to it when he and Nell Choate were married.

The courtship went well. They went to goat ropings, county fairs and dances. And, of course, Red didn't miss a rodeo. He had a good roping horse and won a lot of first monies.

Nell wore the gold locket everywhere that he had sent her for Christmas. That was her engagement ring. She figured he didn't know he was supposed to give her one, so she said nothing about it. If it had been customary to give your betrothed a horse, he would have remembered and done it – but a ring? That was for sissies and city folks. He had already bought her a wide gold wedding band that they would soon use.

They set September for the date they would be married. A few days before, Red took off a couple of work days from the Three Cs to ride over to Tombstone, the county seat, to get their marriage license.

He was just walking out of the courthouse when he met a man wearing a big star on his shirt that denoted his capacity as the County Sheriff.

"You Red Howell?" The sheriff asked after they had howdied and shook.

"That's right. I'm Red Howell. Why do you want to know?" Red's feathers were ruffled. He'd never been questioned by a sheriff or any other law man.

"You know Tom Price?"

"Yeah," Red replied, "I know him. Why?" Red felt a cold chill of dread. He knew Tom Price, his soon-to-be brother-in-law was up for cattle rustling and he didn't want to admit publicly that he'd be related by marriage.

"Well, Mr. Howell, Tom Price named you as a character witness and I have a subpoena for you to appear in court next week."

"Hell," Red exclaimed, "I can't do it. I'm getting married Sunday.

Besides, I don't know Tom Price that well."

"Well," the Sheriff eyed Red dubiously, "Tom is married to Nell Choate's sister, Ola. I reckon you should know him."

"That don't mean a damned thing," Red barked. "I sure as hell ain't marrying the whole family or the in-laws. As soon as we get married on Sunday, we're leaving for my ranch in New Mexico."

The sheriff regarded him coldly. "You are, by law, required to stay in Tombstone until after the trial."

"What about my job?" Red protested. "I work for the Three Cs and they expect me back tomorrow. We're on fall roundup."

"I'll get word to Mr. Boice," the Sheriff said, "and also some word to the Choate ranch. You'd better take your horse over to the livery stable and get yourself a room at the hotel. You ain't going no place."

"Mister, I can't do this to Nell. Let me ride up there tonight," Red pleaded, "I'll be back tomorrow. She's all set to get married Sunday. She already made her dress and everything. The preacher in Light is all set to do the job and we got some folks coming to the wedding." Red had come to the realization that he couldn't get out of this and he was more than a little irritated.

"Sheriff," Red's voice was strained, "I don't know your name, but I never got mixed up with the law in my life and this sure as hell is a bad time to get started."

"You're not mixed up with the law, Mr. Howell. All you have to do is appear in court next Wednesday and swear you'll tell the truth about what you know of Mr. Price. The papers there in your hand will tell you where and what time. I'll see you there," the Sheriff said as he walked away.

Red felt like the bottom had fallen out of his world.

In court, Mr. Boice heard Red's remarks as a character witness for Tom Price. The stolen cattle had belonged to Boice, who had no doubt that Price had stolen the cattle even though Price was ultimately found "Not guilty."

Boice couldn't get it out of his craw and he couldn't stomach the idea of Red, Price's kin by marriage, coming back to the Three Cs to work, so he told him to pick up his last paycheck and not to ever return to the ranch.

The day after the trial, Red rode to the Three Cs headquarters, got his pay and his scant gatherings and rode over to Tom Price's ranch. He found Tom at the corral shoeing a horse.

"Get down, Red," Tom said with a mouth full of horseshoe nails. I'm almost through and we'll go to the house and bum a cup of coffee from Ola."

"Nope," Red replied, "I can't do it, Tom. I'd like to ask a favor, though. Can I stow my gear here? I got fired at the Cs and had to pick up my stuff. I don't have any place to leave it and I've got to go see if Nell still wants to marry me. I'm in a hell of a mess."

"Sure you can, Red, or come down and stay with us 'til you get married. I'm sure sorry about the trouble I got you into."

"While I was waiting around Tombstone for that trial, I met an old boy, name of Godfrey. He's the superintendent of the mine at Gleeson. He said that if I had some ore wagons and teams, he'd give me the contract to haul ore to the smelter at Douglas. He put me onto some equipment that a fellow had at Pearce, so I'm going to see Nell first and then go on down to Pearce to try to make a deal. I can't ask her to wait too much longer."

I'll help any way I can, Red. You might have trouble convincing Nell to live in town, but then Gleeson isn't much of a town, is it?" Tom asked.

"I didn't pay attention when I rode through there going and coming from Tombstone," Red said as he unloaded his gear. "I'll see you in a day or two."

Tom's gaze followed Red until he was out of sight. "Poor son-of -a-gun," he directed his comment at the horse he was shoeing. "That's a hell of a thing, for a cowboy to end up driving an ore wagon."

Chapter Twenty-three

Cowboy Wedding

October 10, 1912

The morning – sunny, clear and crisp – was typical for Southern Arizona. "It's a beautiful day for a wedding," Nell exclaimed as she waited for Red's buggy.

Plans had changed a great deal. The wedding, originally planned for September, had been postponed until October. It was too late in the season to make the move to Red's ranch in the Guadalupes.

"Nell," Red explained, "I don't think we can risk the trip this late, especially with your cattle and horses. We've already seen an early snow and since I about froze to death last winter, I'm mighty cuidado about the weather. Trying to make it through the mountains with a covered wagon and all our possessions is just asking for trouble."

The week before, Red had completed the deal with Marcos Carrillo to buy two ore wagons and six spans of mules. Red had an ore-hauling contract. Godfrey, for his part, was so happy to have an experienced, reliable mule-skinner like Red under contract that he threw in a nice little house to sweeten the pot. He figured if Red's new bride was safely settled and content, Red would be happier with his work.

Red drove his hired buggy from the livery stable and went out to pick up Nell at El Coronado Ranch. She was impatient to leave and could hardly wait for him to get out of the buggy and hand her in. Red marveled at her fresh beauty and sweet enthusiasm. Her parents chose not to attend the wedding to register their disapproval of Nell's choice of a husband. Even her parents' decision didn't dampen Nell's joy.

As they headed out, Red told her, "We'll get to the church in Light in plenty of time to attend the preaching and then we'll ask the minister to do a short wedding service for us."

"Yes," Nell replied. "I figure that will work well because everybody from the area will be there for church anyway and they'll enjoy helping us celebrate."

As they pulled up at the church, they realized that there were no other buggies parked around and there weren't any horses at the hitching post.

"What the heck happened?" Red asked in confusion. He handed the reins to Nell and walked over to a house where smoke was coming out the chimney. He knocked and a grey-haired woman opened the door.

Red hastily swept his ten-gallon hat off his head and asked, "Do you know why the church isn't open today? Ain't it Sunday?"

"Well, I do declare," the lady laughed. "I know you, young man. You're Red Howell, aren't you? You're Nell Choate's beau."

"Not for long," Red blurted.

"Oh dear," she clutched her apron, "what has happened?"

"Well, ma'am, Miss Nell and I are going to get married today, so I wouldn't be her beau any longer. I'll be her husband." He laughed heartily.

"Oh, pshaw, how you young men do go on. The preacher and everyone has gone down to Pearce for an all-day singing and dinner-on-the-grounds at the new church. I'm too old to make that trip, I guess. I sure wanted to go, but nobody asked me."

"Bless your heart, ma'am. When Miss Nell and I get married, we'll take you over to Pearce." Red was always a soft touch for women. "Well, ma'am, thank you for the information. Nell and I have put off this getting married long enough. I reckon we'll have to head on over to Pearce." He put on his hat, tipped it and strode to the buggy.

"That suits me just fine," Nell said when Red explained what had happened. "I don't care what we have to do just as long as we do it together." Red slapped the buggy horse with the end of the reins and they were off to Pearce.

They were a little more than halfway there when they met the procession coming home to Light from Pearce.

Red pulled his buggy out of the road and when the preacher came along, he got out and hailed him down.

"Preacher, I'm Red Howell. Miss Nell Choate and I came down from Turkey Creek to go to church at Light and then we were going to ask you to marry us. When we got to the church everyone was gone and the church was as empty as a last year's bird nest."

"Yes, son, we've all been to a singing convention at Pearce. Come on up to the church and I'll perform the marriage ceremony," the reverend said.

"No, Sir, I don't want to wait any longer. We've had a lot of delays and I want to get it over with. What's wrong with you marrying us right here? I've got the license and everything. Even a ring." Red looked as pitiful as he could.

The preacher laughed. "Well, why not? You'll even have guests." He motioned toward the road behind them. There was buggy after buggy, wagon after wagon, and horsebackers all lined up, wondering what the hold-up was.

It was hard to recognize Red Howell in a black suit, white shirt and tie. They'd all seen him at rodeos and dances with Nell Choate, but he'd never looked like that before.

The preacher said, "Mr. Howell back your buggy into that section corner there. I'll explain to the congregation what's going on and we'll have a real cowboy ranch wedding."

Nell whispered to Red, "Reckon it'll be legal to marry out here miles from nowhere?"

"If it ain't, we'll never know, now will we?" Red said, faking a wicked smirk.

The crowd, sitting in their conveyances, grew quiet when the Reverend held up his hand. All you could hear were the horses stomping, their tails switching off the late crop of flies.

Red had backed his buggy into a corner where two barbed-wire fences came together. Red and Nell stood in the wagon as the preacher began.

"Let us pray," the Reverend said.

"Oh Lord, let it be short," Red groaned.

Nell kicked his boot and Red looked at her with a twinkle in his brown eyes and winked.

"Dearly beloved, we are gathered here. . . . Pardon me, Mr. Howell, would you please remove your hat?"

It got Red's goat to be upbraided like a school boy. *Here I am standing in front of all these people about to get married in the middle of nowhere and that skinny little preacher orders me to take off my hat.*

Nell felt Red tense up. He sure likes to have the last word.

At that moment Red swept his Stetson off in a grand gesture and sailed it out across the prairie.

The Reverend, initially startled, wanted to laugh. He heard the appreciative chuckles of the folks clustered around the wagon. He smiled at the young couple and launched into the ceremony. When the last I-dos and amens were said, Red handed Nell down from the wagon. The womenfolk gathered around to offer their advice and congratulations.

Red accepted handshakes and hearty pats on the back. One of the boys retrieved Red's hat and brought it back to him. Red gratefully put it on.

Red strode over and enveloped the preacher's hand in his big paw and shook it enthusiastically. "Thank you, Reverend." He pressed a ten-dollar bill into the preacher's hand.

Damn, that ten bucks is a third of a month's wages, I sure hope it was worth it.

As Red turned to leave, the preacher said, "Hold on there Mr. Howell. I'm not done with you yet. We have to sign your license with two witnesses and put the notary seal on it. I'll meet you at the church."

Red didn't comment. He went back to the buggy, pulled Nell up to him, kissed her good, and headed down the road – in the opposite direction than the church group was going.

"Let's go home, sweetie, he said to Nell. "Those papers can wait to be signed another day."

Chapter Twenty-four

The Homing

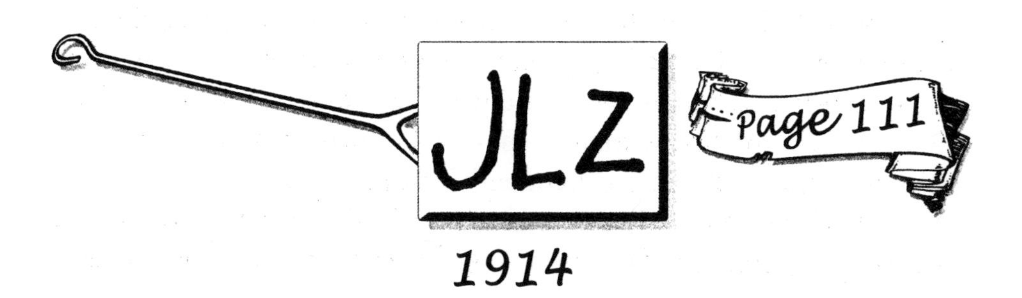

1914

Red took time out from hauling ore to ride over to Nell's homestead with her. He rode the trails, checking to make sure everything was okay. Nell spent the day in her little shack, cleaning it and savoring the time away from the town and it's noisy, inquisitive citizens.

Red, riding up a brushy canyon looking for a cow and calf they missed in the fall round-up, was deep in thought.

Damn, it's already 1914 and I still haven't gone back to my ranch. Well, I made a few quick trips on the train so they would know I was still alive. Hell, Don is taking care of things. He's a good friend.

I've made enough money driving ore wagons to quit and move back to the ranch. I could buy some more cattle and land. Land's cheap now, but there are plenty of folks moving into that part of the country. There's a war in Europe and there's talk of us joining in if England gets involved. They say there'll be a big demand for livestock.

I need to make a move now. I'm going back and talk to Nell. We could go in March.

Energized by his decision, Red made short work of finding the cow and calf.

One evening after a grueling day on the long haul to Douglas, Red and Nell sat quietly at the table after the dishes had been washed. Red cleared his throat.

"Sweetie, I think I've had enough of this mule skinning. I'm thinking it's time for me to go home and show off my wife and son."

"Yes, Lewis," Nell replied, "Leonard will be almost eight-months-old by then and we can make the trip fine. I'm ready for a little adventure myself. How about you?"

"I'm just about at my wits end here. Everyday it's the same road, the same schedule. It's monotomous."

Nell smiled. Monotomous was a joke between them. Early on in their relationship, Red had mispronounced monotonous. Without thinking, Nell corrected him as she would have corrected one of her students. Red took the correction without comment, but from that point on he persisted in saying monotomous frequently and pointedly.

"Let's go, Nell," Red continued. "I'll give Mr. Godfrey notice, sell all my equipment and buy us a good covered wagon and we'll get on the road."

Now that it was out in the open and decided, Red was rarin' to go. "What about your homestead and cattle? What can we do with them."

"I've talked to papa," Nell said. "He wants the homestead. It joins his ranch. I'll sell him the cattle, too. That way they can stay where they were raised. They're good mountain cattle. He'll give us top price for them. You know how papa is."

"I thought we planned on taking them with us to New Mexico. Red studied Nell's face. "You know every cow, what she's out of, how old she is and how good her calves are. I didn't think you wanted to sell them."

"Oh Lewis," Nell scolded, "they're just cows. Driving them that far would hold us back and I'm anxious to get to your ranch and be permanent for once. We've just been sitting here in Gleeson marking time. Let's get moving. I do want to take three or four of my best saddle horses."

Red looked at Nell with admiration. "Has there ever been a woman on earth like you, Nell?" He pulled her to him and kissed her long and hard. Then he picked his chubby, gurgling son up out of the cradle and tossed him in the air a few times. The baby chortled with delight. Red hugged the boy to him and let out a Texas yell. The baby, Leonard, startled by the sound, puckered up to cry. Red held him at arm's length and talked to him man-to-man. Red didn't abide baby talk.

"Pardner, you'll like it there. It's so far back in the hills all you can hear is an owl hoot and the coyote wail and ..."

" ...the wind blow." Nell finished with a grin.

"You'll be too busy to notice the wind, sweetie," Red added. "Once Leonard gets a little older, we'll all three of us be out there looking for a maverick to brand."

Nell laughed and took Leonard from him. As she gently bathed the boy with a dampened cloth, the soft, yellow glow from the kerosene lamp illuminated the small, warm room. Red wondered if he'd ever be this happy again.

Everything went as planned. Nell hated to leave her little house. She'd been happy here with her new husband and baby and a dear friend, Mrs. Godfrey, the boss's wife who had been like a second mother to Nell. It would be difficult to say goodbye.

Red made money on the sale of the wagons and mules. The man who bought them threw in a team of green colts on the deal. Red thought the long trip would be a great time to break them to work.

They left from Nell's parents' ranch and it was a sad farewell. Nell, twenty-four-years-old, had never been far from home. Her family provided a solid, reliable support system in which she had thrived and grown. She hated to take her son far away from the grandparents who doted on him.

The young couple quickly realized that making the decision to move was much easier than actually making the move. They argued and worried over the best way to move themselves and the livestock. Finally, they decided that they would take turns driving the wagon and herding the horses. Nell would take the first shift on the wagon, figuring that driving the horses away from the ranch would be difficult. The horses would be reluctant to leave the ranch where they had been raised.

The wagon was loaded with all Nell's belongings: saddle, cedar chest and much more. Nell played the guitar and the piano.

"Sweetie,' Red noted, "we sure don't have room for your piano but your guitar would fit real good."

Nell agreed, deciding that she'd keep the guitar on the seat beside her. She envisioned gently strumming the guitar as the wagon rocked and swayed sedately down the wagon road. The music would calm Leonard, as well as the livestock, and add a note of fun and color to a long journey. She smiled to herself as she planned the love songs she'd sing to Red and the lullabies she'd croon for Leonard.

With Leonard and her guitar beside her, Nell sat on the hard wagon seat trying to hold back the tears. Leonard occupied his own padded chair. The chair was secured to a metal brace under the wagon seat.

Nell clucked the green team as she loosened the reins. The horses fidgeted nervously but they didn't move. Grabbing the buggy whip out of its holder, Nell flicked it above the rumps of the team. Still, they did nothing more than jostle into each other and stomp their feet.

Red, riding Domingo, was driving six head of horses. He glanced back and realized that Nell hadn't moved. He whirled Domingo around and loped back to the wagon with the intention of swinging his lariat to put a couple of double-cees on the rumps of the recalcitrant colts.

Red hollered and gave the colts a sound slap. For a moment they stopped moving altogether and then, as if with a single mind, they lunged forward and pounded down the road at a full gallop. Nell regained her balance and tried to rein in the horses, but they had their heads and no intention of slowing down or stopping. Nell, sawing on the reins, glanced over and noted that Leonard was bouncing up and down in his chair and gurgling with delight. Nell turned her attention back to the narrow, winding road. Her eyes teared from the wind as bushes and trees whizzed by at an alarming speed. She braced her feet against the front of the wagon and pulled on the reins with all her strength, but to no avail. She'd been vaguely aware of her guitar bouncing on the seat when it suddenly went airborn as they turned a curve in the road. Instantly she felt the slight vibration and heard the sickening crunch of the guitar as it was crushed by the back wheel of the wagon.

Red finally found a wide place in the road where he could race past the wagon and gain a place beside the runaway team. Crowding Domingo in close, he grabbed the headstall of the near horse and gradually pulled the team to a standstill.

Piling off his horse, Red jumped into the wagon and gathered Nell and Leonard into his arms. He felt the sting of tears behind his eyelids.

Nell and Leonard are more precious to me than anything else in this world, and I put them in danger. So much of the grand leave-taking to show Nell's parents how well I can take care of my family.

When Red unlocked his family from his embrace, Nell looked back at the road and commented, "Well, I guess there won't be any lullabies or love songs."

Red and Nell both laughed in relief. Red got back in the saddle and rounded up the herd of horses and tied them head-to-tail. He rode beside the wagon with the horses in tow, just in case there was another wreck.

They made it to an old windmill near Willcox where they camped for the first time. Red grazed the horses nearby while Nell pulled out the Dutch oven and warmed food from a basket lovingly prepared by her mother. It was filled with fried chicken and all the trimmings.

They started to eat. All of a sudden, Nell wasn't hungry. She left her plate of food on the ground near Red and walked out among the grazing horses. Tears streamed down her face as she stroked each horse in turn. *This is the only familiar thing from home that I have*, she thought.

Red had never seen this side of his wife. He thought she was tough as nails and he didn't know how to handle it.

Leonard saved the day. He reached his little arms out to his father and said, "Dada."

"I'll be damned," Red exclaimed, "That kid called me daddy. Hey, Nell, this kid can talk."

Nell forgot her misery and rushed back to the campfire to share this miraculous event with her husband and son.

Days went by. They restocked their larder at Deming before heading northeast to Nutt, on their way to a safe crossing on the Rio Grande. They made good time. The only disagreeable weather factor was the perpetual wind. Even though it was to their backs, the dust was thick and whirlwinds stirred up last year's crop of dry tumble weeds, spooking the horses now and then.

Leonard was Nell's greatest concern. His face, with its sweet, baby, peaches-and-cream complexion was chapped and sunburned.

The white clothes she had so lovingly stitched for him were now a dingy tan from being laundered in the water from dirt tanks where that had camped.

The romance of cooking delicious meals for Red as she had planned had fallen by the wayside. She hated the sight of a Dutch oven. Wood that made good coals – a must for Dutch oven cooking – was scarce and their food seemed to be worse each day than the day before.

All she cooked now was bacon, eggs and biscuits. Half the time, the biscuits were raw in the middle and burned on the outside.

"Lewis," Nell said to Red the night before they reached the Rio Grande River crossing, "when we get there, I'm going to dive into that clear, running water and use a whole bar of soap to get this road dust and muddy-tank-water-scum off of me."

"Hell, hon, that ol' river is probably muddy itself from all the snow melt where it heads up in the Colorado mountains. Besides, it's too cold this time of year to swim. You'd better keep heating water in the kettle and take a warm bath in the wash tub."

Nell snorted, "You just wait and see."

"Yep," Red replied, "it won't be just me who'll see. Everyone on this road will stop to see a wild woman thrashing among the icebergs. They'll think I threw you in."

Nell worked silently at her chores. She knew how to get his attention.

"If it'll make you feel any better," Red conceded, "then just go ahead and try it. Just remember, you're not swimming in Turkey Creek. The Rio Grande is deep."

They arrived on the bank of the river in the late afternoon and set up camp. Red arranged to have their wagon helped across the river the next day.

Meanwhile, Nell got her towel and soap.

"Lewis, watch Leonard. If he wakes up, just come on down around that bunch of willows. That's where I'm going to bathe. You know, it wouldn't hurt you to wash off a little of that road dust."

"I took a bath at that boarding house we stayed in at Deming," Red bristled.

"Guess you think that'll do you for another year. Adios. I'm going."

Nell sang as she followed the river to the willow thicket upstream.

Now, what the hell am I going to do? Red watched the tall, lithe woman disappear from sight. It won't hurt to wake the baby just this once. I'm going to see that she's all right.

He picked up the sleeping boy. Leonard didn't awaken.

Little mite is so tired after jolting over every rock in Southern New Mexico in his wagon seat that he's not about to wake up now. Red cradled him gently in his long arms.

Nell was just taking off her chemise when man and child arrived.

"That's enough," Red whispered urgently. "Don't take everything off," he begged.

She tossed the chemise onto the bush where she had hung her outer garments and dived into the Rio Grande.

There had never been water this cold in Turkey Creek, even in the winter. I'm darned sure never letting Lewis know I want to get right back out and put my clothes on real fast. If it kills me, I'll make him think it is just wonderful.

She paddled up to the river's edge where she'd left her soap and towel. She did a quick all-over with the soap. She was rinsing off when she saw Red gather her clothes off the bush and head back to camp.

"You sorry son-of-a-gun," she yelled. "I'll get even with you and if you think I'm going to stay in this thicket 'til dark, you're crazy."

She got out of the water, wrapped the towel around her as best she could and bare-footed it into camp.

"Gosh, this feels good," she said as she stood by the camp fire. "I think I'll just cook supper like this."

"Oh, Nell, please, Here comes someone. Your clothes are in the wagon. Hurry before they see you."

Still standing by the fire, she said, "Bet they'll think towels are short where we came from. It's not easy to get one all the way around a 5'10" woman."

"Now, Nell ..."

Nell had teased him long enough. She was cold, but he'd never know it. She wandered slowly over and climbed into the wagon. She could almost hear his sigh of relief. She had escaped seeing a Red Howell fit by a hair.

They left the river, circled the white sands and arrived in Alamogordo. They put their horses in a livery stable and checked into a hotel.

Nell bathed Leonard in the big bath tub. He was delighted by the warm water and mounds of suds. Nell added a potion of rose water and glycerin to the bath water. Regardless of Nell's efforts, Leonard emerged from the luxurious bath looking like a little orphan – rusty and sunburned.

Nell was equally shocked when she looked in the mirror. Her black hair, Indian straight, still had the residue of dirty water and dusty travel. Her carefully cared-for skin looked like twenty-four-year-old rawhide.

When they went down stairs to eat, they didn't looked out of place with the other diners. The other travelers saw a big, red-headed cowboy, all clean and shiny accompanied by his tall, thin wife. Nell, in a frilly, white shirtwaist and a long black skirt, carried their sleeping baby wrapped in a blue blanket.

They couldn't eat enough fried chicken and gravy. They marveled at biscuits that were not burned on thevtop and bottom and raw in the middle. It seemed odd to eat food that didn't taste of campfire smoke and wood ashes.

Leaving Alamogordo the next day, they made good time in spite of the fact that it was all uphill to High Rolls. They made camp early. Tomorrow they would cross the summit of the Sacramento mountains. It would be a dangerous trip.

The wagon was fully loaded and heavy and the team was young and green. Working their way up the steep, winding road kept Red and Nell busy.

Red tied his lariat to his saddle horn and secured it on the wagon tongue to help the team pull the load over some of the steeper places.

Nell was not without fear. One little mistake, one break of Red's lariat or one of the young horses getting boogered would send the wagon plunging off the narrow road into a canyon half-a-mile deep.

She whipped the team when Red told her to and kept sawing on the reins to keep them from hugging the left bank.

When they finally topped out, Red went back to get the saddle horses. He'd tied each horse to a tree about a mile back at the point where the road became steep.

Nell stopped the wagon, reached over and got Leonard, hugging him close. She got down from the wagon. The team was sweating and heaving from the exertion. She patted each horse and crooned her thanks.

"I'll never forget you. You're the pair of broncs that worked so hard to get us safely over the mountains. I promise I'll keep you on the ranch with us."

Three days later they drove into Red's parents' ranch. Sarah and Bill Howell had been keeping an eye out for them ever since they had received Nell's letter saying that the three of them were on their way. When they saw the dust, they headed down the road to meet their new daughter-in-law and grandson.

When they met on the road, Red jumped off his horse, gathered his ma in his arms and hugged her to him. "I've never been so glad to see anyone in my whole life." Then he embraced his pa.

Nell sat on the wagon seat holding her son. She didn't know how to handle this. Although she had corresponded with them since she and Red had married two years ago, she still felt like an outsider.

Red finally remembered his manners. "Pa and ma, come say howdy to your daughter-in-law, Nell, and your grandson, Leonard."

Nell climbed down from the wagon feeling like a poor refugee from a foreign country.

"Mrs. Howell," she said, "I'm sorry we are all so sunburned, chapped and grimy. It has been a long haul."

Nell handed Leonard to Sarah and said, "I wanted him to be so clean and cute when we got here, but he looks like a little street urchin."

"He sure looks good to me," Sarah Howell said as she passed the wriggling boy to his grandfather. "I'm sure I looked just like Leonard when I met my grandmother Zumwalt. I probably looked worse because I had just ridden a horse across Texas with my mother and I wasn't a year old yet."

Some of the Howell boys - Tom, Sam & Levi

My boy Leonard with me

Me on the left and some of my hands at Four Wells

Chapter Twenty-five

How Do You Stop This Critter?

1915

Time seemed to fly by. Red bought ranches and cattle like there was no tomorrow. The escalating war in Europe had boosted the price of beef. At any given time, Red was on a buying trip somewhere in New Mexico, Arizona or Texas. Nell ran the ranch.

Red was big-time now. He replaced his car as soon as a newer model came out and there was always a newer, better car coming out on the market.

Country roads were little better than wagon trails, but Red bounced back and forth between the ranches he'd bought.

Nell kept hoping Red would buy something with a nice house nearer town. Instead, he bought out hardscrabble homesteaders – starve-outs he called them. In comparison, the house at Four Wells – such as it was – was better than any of Red's acquisitions.

When Red had to travel any distance he would go by train, buy a bunch of cattle, load them on the train and ship them home. It sure beat working them on horseback.

On these long trips, Red had plenty of time to reminisce. So much had happened since he and Nell had arrived at Four Wells in 1914.

I'll never forget Nell's face. She tried to hide it, but I could see the shock and disappointment on her face as Four Wells came into view.

She seemed almost reluctant to climb down from the wagon. It had been our home for 21 days. She glanced from the wagon to the three-room shack like she was trying to decide which one was worse.

Red winced as he recalled the desolate scene.

I tried to make light of it, but it felt like I had failed her.

Red marveled at the way he could read Nell.

Nell isn't one for a lot of talking, but she can say volumes in a glance and a shrug of her shoulders. Dammit, I love her, but she can be aggravating. It don't make no sense, but I sure feel like an old bull in a chute about half the time when we're together.

Red felt a chill go down his spine. *I came back to the ranch from riding up in the foothills all day. Me and that cowhand of ours. Lefty. We'd been branding. The minute I rode in, I knew something wasn't quite right. She'd had something on her mind for the past few days. We ate and she cleaned up the kitchen. I heard the dish water splash as she threw it on that puny little tree out by the back door. She dried her hands on her apron and pulled up a chair.*

"Lewis," she said, "we must get something to cover these floors. Leonard needs to learn to walk. He's already crawling and I can't forever keep him corralled on a quilt. Let's get some linoleum for these three rooms."

"Linoleum?" I hollered like I'd been bee-stung. "Linoleum in a shack like this? What do you think we're made of? Money?"

She gave me a look like I was an idiot child and laughed. She laughed at me. She knew she'd gotten my goat.

"How in the hell am I supposed to get linoleum here from Carlsbad? On pack mules?" I knew my voice was getting louder than it needed to be.

"No Lewis," she said real patiently in that voice she used to settle a spooky old cow, "in the wagon. There's a lot of things we need. We should go into town and buy them before we take the cover off the wagon." I could tell she was primed.

I could feel my temper rising, but I tried to reason with her. "Nell, I was going to ride into town tomorrow and try to find somebody who wants to sell some cattle. I think that should come first, don't you?"

"No, Lewis, I don't. The first and foremost thing should be to make a home. I can't live like this with a baby. If it was just us, it'd be fine for a while, but I will not struggle with the dirt and the wind blowing through the cracks. There are a lot of things that should be done here before we buy more cattle. You've got good barns and corrals. Why can't I do a few things to make this house liveable? If you don't want to spend your money, I'll use the money from the sale of my homestead and cattle. I had hoped to have it for an emergency..."

I interrupted her. "I'll take care of the damned emergencies, Nell.

What kind of a hair pin do you think you married?"

I was halfway afraid she'd answer that question. I decided a little backtracking was in order. "I guess I flew off the handle. I want you to be happy here. It's a pretty sorry place to bring a bride, way to hell and gone…"

Then she interrupted me. "As you well know, I'm used to living way to hell and gone. Let's not change the subject. I want to go to town in the wagon tomorrow. You can scout around for cattle and I'll take care of the things we need to fix up the house. I've got a long list."

"Go to town in a covered wagon? I yelled at her. "Do you know the ribbing I'd get if my compadres see us in town in a covered wagon?

Nell laughed again. "What would they say, sweetie?"

I sensed the anger in her reply, but I couldn't stop. "They'd say, 'Well, Red , it didn't take, did it? You're taking her back to Arizona?' Is that what you want them to say?"

She stared at me with sadness in her eyes. I realized in that instant how tired and drawn she looked. She grabbed the water bucket and as the screen door banged behind her, she yelled, "Don't put Leonard on the floor. I'm tired of pulling splinters out of his hands and knees."

Looking back, Red realized he was as proud of Nell's home improvement accomplishments as she was. At the time, it had seemed like they'd never be done with it.

It took lots of hard work, but with the help of the cowboys, it was accomplished. Red chuckled as he remembered watching the tough, bandy-legged men draw straws to see who tacked up cheese cloth, mixed flour paste or hung the brightly colored wall paper. Somehow Nell pulled everything together.

On the outside of the house, Nell asked the men to nail lathe over the cracks between the boards. It made a nice pattern. Hell, I thought she was done, but she had the crew paint the whole damned house with linseed oil and a redwood stain.

Red knew she wanted a front porch added to the house, but by this time he was losing patience and the ranch needed their full attention. Nell knew she was crowding her luck as it was.

With the back porch screened and the weather warming up, they ate many meals out there. It made the house seem larger when they weren't all crowded into the kitchen.

Their family was growing. Nell was pregnant again. Red didn't seem particularly thrilled. After the excitement of first baby, he didn't show much interest. Nell hoped this one would go full term. She'd lost a couple of babies since Leonard had been born. The intense bleeding and cramping pain when she lost a baby seemed to suck the life out of her. She didn't say anything to Red. He usually wasn't home anyway and it wasn't like she could commiserate with the hands. Her one outlet was writing to her mother-in-law, Sarah. She didn't dwell on it, but it helped to share the burden with another woman. Red usually wasn't home and when he was, he made it clear that he wasn't interested in "female disorders."

The ranch was growing, too. With each property and bunch of cattle that Red bought, he had to have more help. That made more work for Nell, but she never complained. She wrote to Sarah: I sure don't want another woman in here to help. It would just crowd up the house and there's little enough room as it is.

Red had built a third room before he and Nell married. Now, it was the bunk house. Nell called it "The Boys Dorm." It had a couple of bunk beds, each with a war bag or two at the end. The men pounded nails into Nell's new wallpaper and hung their Sunday clothes.

In one of her letters to Sarah, Nell wrote: Someday I'm going to write a manual called, "How to Tame a Cowboy." Living in such close quarters with them, I certainly have plenty of experience.

I'm always happy when payday rolls around. Red takes the cowboys into town for a two or three-day spree. It's heavenly to have the place mostly to myself. I can spend time with Leonard without interruption. I even have a few minutes to read and write a letter to you.

Nell didn't include anything in her letter about how Red tied one on with the boys. She was certain he was doing more than drinking, but there wasn't anything she could do about it.

Instead of worrying about Red, Nell saddled one of her Arizona horses, put Leonard on the saddle in front of her and rode out to see how the cattle looked. She checked the dirt tanks to see if they had filled with rain water from the little draws that feed them. She rode to this section of the ranch or that to see how the grass looked.

When she found a calf with screw worms, she herded the calf and its mama back to the corrals for the boys to doctor when they got home from town.

As she turned the cattle into the corral, she grinned and said to Leonard, "Well, I don't suppose those boys will be too happy to see these wormy animals. They tell me the smell of that creosote they use for medicine on those cattle doesn't set too well with a hangover." Leonard didn't know what she was talking about but he enjoyed the attention.

Red's penchant for new cars meant there was always a new model parked by the side of the house. Nell learned to drive the Model T Fords. As they got richer, Red decided that a Model T didn't suit him, so he bought a REO. The REO didn't operate like a Model T with its brake and clutch controls. The REO had gears.

Red didn't bother to show Nell how to drive it. He brought it home, parked the car, and rode off with the cowboys and neighbors who had come to help brand. Nell had agreed to meet them at the South Well at noon.

She was an excellent ranch cook. Her beans didn't rattle in the tin plates. She made delicious steak and gravy and her biscuits rose almost to the lid of the Dutch oven – they were light and fluffy. Red loved cobbler and Nell always had dried peaches and apples around for baking.

Nell worked to get everything ready for lunch. She packed it all up and loaded it into the car. Finally she secured Leonard by tying him in the front seat with a dish towel. She cranked the monster and took off for the South Well.

South Well was in a distant pasture and to get there, Nell had to go through a hard-to-open Texas gate. As she approached the gate, she wondered whether she should stop the car and turn it off or if she could leave it on while she opened the gate. It certainly would be quicker and easier, she mused, if I could leave everything running.

Try as she might, she couldn't figure out how to stop the car and keep the engine running. To save time, she decided to slow the car down so that it was barely moving. She figured she could jump out, open the gate, let the car creep through, quickly close the gate, run and catch up with the car and be on her way. The land was gradually rising and indeed, the car was moving at a snail's pace. The ruts in the road would keep the vehicle on track.

In the back of her mind, Nell realized that this probably wasn't one of her best ideas but she was tired and single-minded in her determination to finish the task she'd started.

Nell jumped out of the car and raced up to the gate.

Damnit, this ornery old thing won't open. She struggled frantically to free the loop of wire off the two poles and open the gate. She glanced up and was horrified to see the big old car only a few feet away. She jumped back and the car continued inexorably. The wire screeched against the metal body of the car as the Reo strained briefly against the gate. Wires popped and the posts snapped as the car crept through. Like a grande dame draped in a wire boa, the car continued on, trailing the remains of the gate. Nell recovered her wits, ran after the car and jumped in.

Now that Leonard was safe, her fear turned to anger and her anger was directed at Red. She continued on the roundup. When she arrived, she circled the big flat where they were holding the cattle. As she passed Red, she shouted out the window, "How the heck do you stop this thing?"

On her next turn, Red jumped on the running board and told her which pedal to push. She steered the car with great precision to a spot near the campfire. The men were standing around watching the show and laughing their heads off. They knew that, more than likely, they'd witness a Red Howell fit when the dust settled.

That's me on the left with Nell's folks, Nell and Leonard at Four Wells.

Chapter Twenty-six

The Chewing

1915 - 1917

It was always a delight for Red, Nell and Leonard to see Red's parents. The elder Howells had moved from their ranch at Hope to the Yellow Lake Ranch north of Roswell. It more difficult for them to visit now because Yellow Lake Ranch was farther away.

Sarah and Bill Howell adored Nell and their grandsons. Nell's last pregnancy had gone full term and Leonard was happy to have a little brother, William.

Four Wells was remote and the road that led to it was terrible, but the Howells had a sturdy car and they were familiar with rough travel. Nell was embarrassed that she couldn't offer Sarah and Bill better accommodations. She and Lewis slept on a pallet on the floor in the kitchen and gave Red's parent's their bedroom.

Red's father seemed to be taking stock of the way Red and Nell lived. He knew Red's holdings reached from the Guadalupe foothills to the alkali flats near the Pecos River.

Bill commented to his wife as they settled in, "I don't understand it, Sarah. These kids live like folks did back in the 1880s."

Sarah shushed him and whispered, "Nell doesn't look well. She's just skin and bones and her color isn't good. She doesn't complain, but I'm worried about her."

The next morning Red and his Pa rode out to check some waterings. They rode in silence until Bill cleared his throat and turned to

Red.

"Red, how are you doing financially? It looks like you are spreading out fast. Are you paying for all this?"

"You know, pa, I'm holding my own. I don't mortgage the whole ranch when I buy another piece of land. I just put up one of the places I've bought."

Red considered it a moment and proudly announced, "You know, I'm doing good."

"Well, son, why don't you ever buy an outfit with a decent house on it? Besides Sarah, Nell's one of the best women I've ever seen. I can't rightly figure out why she has to live out here, way to hell-and-gone from anything. In spite of having a baby and a toddler, she works like a slave feeding cowboys. Why, you don't even have water piped to the house. Nell carries every drop of water from the windmill out in back. It wouldn't surprise me if she has to chop her own firewood."

"Now, pa, let up on me. I'm making money and putting together a big outfit. I'll get around to building her a real mansion someday."

Bill grimaced. "Sure, Red, if she lasts that long. She's too good a woman to be worn out while she's so young. What the hell, you're gone most of the time, either looking for cattle, pulling a rodeo, ropin' or off to God-knows-where. She's there…"

Red cut him short. "Pa, I'm making her a living."

Bill snorted. "It's a hell of a living for a woman. She even has to saddle up and ride when you're short-handed. I know she likes to work cattle, but did you ever try it with a little shaver clinging to you so he don't fall off?

"Cut it out, Pa, she's happy."

"Well, I'll be damned, what choice does she have, cut off from everything? You take better care of your horses than you do her. At least with your horses, you wouldn't think of working them day after day without switching to another horse."

"Oh, pa," Red snickered, "I switch women now and then, too."

"I'll bet you do," Billy said grimly. "I don't care much for your humor."

They rode in uncomfortable silence until Bill said, "Your mother and I decided last night that we are going to take Nell and the boys back to Yellow Lakes with us. They can stay there for a couple of weeks while Nell recovers her health. I don't think she healed up after the baby was born."

"Hell, pa," Red said loudly, "she wouldn't go with you. She'd be too afraid somebody would get some dirt on her floor. She's particular about her house."

"That house is the sorriest place I ever saw a white woman have to live in. I'm ashamed of you, Red. You're a self-centered son-of-a-gun. You always have been. I hoped that when you had a family, you'd think of somebody else for a change. Truthfully, I don't see you making much of a change."

Red was stunned.

Pa is one of the gentlest people on earth and for him to ride me like this, he must be real mad.

Feeling like the wind had been knocked out of him, Red loped on ahead to the dirt tank.

Later, when they returned home, Red had thawed a bit. As they rode over the low hill behind the house, he surveyed the scene with fresh eyes. The house was still a pitiful little claim shack. He grimaced as he recalled the plush hotels where he stayed while he was rodeoing and buying cattle.

Oh hell, one of these days it'll be better for her, Red thought. *I still love her – more than any woman on earth. Hell, she's all right with our life the way it's going. I've never heard her complain.*

It didn't take much persuasion to convince Nell to go with Bill and Sarah. When she left with them, she sat back and tried to relax. She didn't feel well. Leonard was sitting in the front seat with his grandpa, thoroughly enjoying every minute of the trip. Sarah took care of the baby while Nell napped.

Sarah leaned forward and spoke softly to her husband. "Bill, stop at the hospital in Roswell and lets have Doc Woods look at Nell."

Nell didn't object when they stopped at the hospital and Sarah accompanied her to the doctor's office located in an office adjoining the hospital. Doc Woods examined Nell and listened to her. Half-an-hour later, the doctor accompanied Nell out to the lobby where Sarah waited with the baby.

"This young lady has been working too hard for too long. She's worn down. She lost a lot of blood with the last baby. She needs sleep, sunshine and good, healthy food and pick up a bottle of Lydia Pickham for her."

Sarah was relieved. "Thank you, Doctor Wood. We'll take good care of her."

Nell was exhausted and she surprised herself by relaxing. Sarah bustled around like a mother hen and Nell basked in the attention, as did Leonard and the baby.

A week later, Nell was feeling better. Sarah was on the porch with the children. Nell gently took Sarah's rough hand in hers. "Mrs. Howell, thank you so much. I feel like I'm coming out of a long, dark tunnel. You and Mr. Howell are angels. I didn't realize how much I'd let myself get rundown."

The next day, the family sat out on the front porch after their evening meal.

"Dear God," Bill said, "who is that driving up the lane? Why, I do believe the prodigal son is returning."

Red pulled up in front of the porch and unfolded his 6'4" frame from a shiny, new car.

"Well, Red," Bill observed, dryly "that's quite a chariot you're driving. I expect we should bow down to his majesty." Bill boiled every time he thought of how tired and worn down Nell had been.

'Oh, Bill," Sarah scolded, "you behave yourself now. You've caused enough trouble with him already. Just let it lay for Nell's sake."

For her part, Nell was happy to see Red, but she felt almost bashful. She knew she looked pale and washed out.

Red turned to her. "Hey, sweetie, you look like something the cat drug up."

Bill bristled. "She looks a lot better than she did when we brought her home. The way you were taking care of her, you're lucky she isn't dead."

Red tensed up, ready for a fight. A glance at Nell diffused his anger. "I'm sorry, sweetie."

Nell wanted to change the subject. "Isn't that a new car, Lewis?"

"That's your new car, sweetie." I'm not leaving you afoot when I have to be gone. Do you like it?"

Mr. Howell broke into the conversation. "A damn car isn't what she needs. I told you the other day what she needs."

"Well, pa," Red said with uncharacteristic patience, "there's a new ranch to go with this car."

"Oh yeah, Red, and where is this ranch? In Dog Canyon? That's the only place left on this earth that's more remote than Four Wells."

"No, pa" Red replied, "I bought the old Adams place. It has a real nice house on it, good corrals and a dandy well. It's even got water to the house."

"Well, hot damn, Red, what stung you? The ranch must have come with a roping arena."

"Now, Pa." Red continued. "There's good waterings, good grass, even a pretty good road and it won't be so far for Leonard to go to school in a year or so. And if you really want to know what stung me, it was you, Pa. You got me down where the hair was short. I was ashamed that I had to be chewed out by you."

"Oh, Lewis," Nell was quick to defend him, "your pa didn't say anything you didn't already know."

"Nell, why didn't you say something?"

"I don't exactly enjoy your Red Howell fits and I figured you'd get tired of that rocky road yourself sometime and move us nearer to civilization. I remember the fit you threw when I just wanted to fill up the cracks in the wall and put linoleum on the floors. I didn't dare ask for a house. You might of had a stroke."

The boys and I
did real good
at this rodeo.

Chapter Twenty-seven

You're Joshing Me. A Real House?

Nell was eager to see her new house on the Quarter Circle-A, the Adam's Ranch near Lakewood, but she had to wait. Red explained that it would be another couple of weeks before the deal was closed on the Adam's place and he could take possession.

Nell's in-laws insisted that she and the children continue to stay at Yellow Lakes for a few more weeks. With some reluctance Nell agreed. She missed Four Wells, but when she looked at the situation in the cold light of day, she knew she was still weak and tired. It felt good to be on the mend and she'd need her strength for the move.

Since they had to wait anyway, Red figured he might as well put his favorite roping horse on the train at Carlsbad and go to El Paso via Pecos to meet up with his partners, Ed Echols and Jesse Gerdner. They'd all entered in a big steer roping.

As the train headed West, Red fretted about Four Wells. *I sure wish Nell wasn't at Yellow Lake. She should be home at Four Wells taking care of the place while I'm gone. She sure can straighten out those cowboys. They don't mind taking orders from her because she knows every foot of the ranch. She can tell you where this-cow-or-that-cow runs.*

Hell, she never gives powders like I do. She just asks Ralph or Punk – even old Beuford – in that nice way of hers where they think there might be a water gap-out or a tank drying up. When she's asking if the boys have found any wormy calves lately at Pin Tank, she makes it sound so friendly.

Beu – he prefers to be called that instead of Beuford – has been on the ranch with me a long while and he's my segundo. He'll take care of things, but I'd sure feel more at ease if I knew Nell was there instead of at Yellow Lake being spoiled by ma and pa.

I probably shouldn't go off roping while Nell's gone. There's so much to do around the ranch and I need to close the deal on the new place.

Red slouched in the train seat, trying to stretch out his long legs. He frowned. Gradually his face relaxed an he smiled to himself.

I'll bet this trip will put me on the trail of some good cattle for the new ranch.

After that dressing down pa's been giving me, I need something else to think about. It just get's my goat that he'd light into me that way.

Ah, what the hell. At least with Nell and the boys at Yellow Lake, I don't have to worry about them being stuck out at Four Wells. If Nell feels poorly, it's only 45 minutes to Roswell.

Red returned from his travels. Nell, refreshed by her stay at Yellow Lakes, returned to the ranch.

"Alright, sweetie," Red told her, " let's go see our new outfit."

Nell was thrilled with the house. It was spacious and had a front and back porch. The house was painted a pale grey with white trim. The big windows made the paneled living room light and airy. The three bedrooms were wall-papered and there were real carpets on the floors.

The dining room was large enough to seat the whole Howell clan, if needs be. The kitchen had a sink. Not only did the water run in from an overhead tank that the windmill pumped into, but the sink also had a drain.

Hallelujah, Nell thought. *I won't have to haul in bucket after bucket of water every day. And, look at that. The sink drains to the outside. I won't have to carry out the water, either.*

Staring at the big, claw-footed bath tub, Nell daydreamed. *The boys will enjoy splashing around in there.*

She moved through the house. *Oh, look at that lovely yard with the white, picket fence. I'll be able to put Leonard out in the yard and he can't wander off. A little child like that doesn't have any sense, but if Leonard's any example, they sure can get in serious trouble quickly. If he wandered off and something happened to him, I just don't think I could bear it. When the baby gets older, he'll enjoy it out there, too.*

Red came up behind Nell and wrapped his arms around her waist. "Do you like it, sweetie?"

Nell nodded, unable to speak.

"And, there something else," Red spoke softly. "There's a bunk house with a kitchen. We'll get some broke-down cowboy who's too stove-up to ride and needs a home. He can cook for the hands. That way, you won't be cooking for the whole crew."

Nell couldn't hold back her tears.

"You don't like it?" Red asked with concern. "I mortgaged the whole outfit for it. I thought maybe it'd start to make up for the way I've made you live since we left Arizona."

"I do like it, Lewis, but I wish you hadn't put everything up for it." Nell said. She sighed, turned, reached up and gently stroked his face. "You never do anything halfway, do you? There's nothing I can do about it. You'll always be Red Howell and it looks like I'll always love you just the way you are."

Out in the corral

Chapter Twenty-eight

World War I

April 6, 1917

"Red, why don't you get one of those government contracts to supply horses to the Remount Stations?" Walter McDonald directed his question in Red's general direction. The Canal Street Saloon was noisy and crowed with cowboys in various stages of drunkenness. Slurring his words, Walter continued, "You got lots of horses and they say the price they're bringing is real good."

"Trouble is, Walter," Red paused for a deep swig, "I need all the good horses I have now. It takes a bunch of horse flesh to work that rough country. Red pushed the brim of his hat up with the back of his hand and screwed up his face in concentration. His face cleared. "I've been thinking about that band of wild horses that run up there around Farris Tank. They sure are good horses, not inbred or anything. They don't have a brand on a one of them. Now, I wonder where they came from?"

"No telling, Red. They could have drifted in here ahead of that last storm looking for grass. They're probably out of the Sacramentos. One thing's for sure – they haven't seen many men. A man on horseback sure spooks them."

"Yeah, Walter, I tried to get a rope on one the other day and he flat outrun me. They sure got good feet. I imagine they were raised in country like this. Those rocks didn't slow them down."

"You'd better look into catching them," Walter declared solemnly, "before someone else thinks of it." Walter downed what was left of his whiskey, slid off his bar stool and, weaving slightly, stuck out his rough hand. "Red, I'll see you next time you're in town. I've gotta go. My woman is surely champing at the bit. I know she's spent all her money and she's ready to hit the road for the ranch."

Red shook Walter's hand and watched as the slightly inebriated cowboy elbowed his way through the crowded saloon as he headed for the door. Red remembered his manners and yelled, "Walter, tell Pearl I said howdy." Walter, as he opened the door, touched the brim of his hat to acknowledge that he'd received the message and would pass it on.

Red hunched over his drink and thought about what Walter had said. *A man just might make a little money on those remount horses. I think I could get enough boys to green-break them and put a little rein on them. It wouldn't cost anything but their wages and chuck. There's always a bunch of those boys just waiting around for some work. They'd be glad to make a few bucks. They're all good hands. It seems like most of them are planning to enlist in the cavalry anyway, so working a few horses would be real good for them.*

I'll run it by Nell. She may not think too highly of the idea because I'll be gone even more than usual. What the hell, that damned woman knows more about the ranches, especially the new one, than I do. Ah, I shouldn't resent her. I couldn't do half as much high-tailing around if I didn't have Nell taking care of everything.

I'd better get on home. I've been at that big roping in Fort Worth for a couple of weeks. I probably shouldn't have gone, but they say it was the last one until the war is over.

Red grinned to himself. *Hot damn, Robinson and I sure won a lot of money. Those two, big matched ropings and couple of day-monies were real profitable. Those Texas ropers were hard to beat but we showed 'em.*

I'll sure be glad to get home.

Nell was glad Red was coming back. He could take over the responsibility for everything. The boys would glad to see their daddy, especially because Red always brought them treats. Nell kept an eye on the road and she was soon rewarded with the sight of a rooster tail of dust rapidly approaching the ranch. She dried her hands, took off her apron and primped quickly in front of the hall mirror.

As she stepped out on the porch, year-old Bill toddled unsteadily after her.

"Bill, you stay on the porch," she admonished sternly.

Five-year-old Leonard had raced past her. He was down the steps and heading for the yard. Red had just driven up in a great cloud of dust. To the boys' delight, he revved the engine a couple of times before he jumped out of the car. He opened the picket gate and grabbed Leonard under the arms. He pivoted several times, swinging Leonard high and low. Leonard hollered in delight and William babbled in excited agreement. Red gathered Leonard into his arms for a big bear-hug as he strode up the steps. On the porch, baby Bill wrapped his pudgy arms around Red's leg. Red shifted Leonard to his left arm and embraced Nell with his right arm.

After a few minutes, the dust started to settle and Red asked, "I don't suppose there are any children here who would like some store-bought candy?" He squatted down on his boot heels and handed each boy a fat peppermint stick. "You two sit down there on the steps and work on those so your mother and I can talk."

Nell brought out cups of coffee and they settled comfortably in a couple of cane chairs. Red handed Nell a book.

"Thank you, Lewis. I sure look forward to getting something new to read. I'll get started on it tonight right after I bed the boys down. I finished the last one you brought me weeks ago."

Looking at the excited children sitting on the steps, Red said, "Those boys are sure growing fast."

"I'm teaching Leonard the alphabet and his numbers. He has learned them well. I read him stories out of that children's book your mother gave us." Nell laughed. "In fact, I've read those stories so many times, he knows the words by memory. If I get bored and skip a page, he corrects me on how the story should go. Every so often I add a new ending to change the story.

"Leonard always says, 'Oh, no, mama. That's not right.' I have never been able to get anything by him."

Red chuckled appreciatively at the picture of domestic life that Nell painted.

They sat in companionable silence for a few minutes before Red asked, "How's everything going on the ranch?"

Nell gave him a quick summary to bring him up to date. "How about you, Lewis? How'd the roping go?"

Red, pleased that she'd asked, was able to tell her that he'd done very well. Suddenly, he slapped his thigh. "I forgot something." He jumped up from his seat and headed back to the car. He ruffled the boys' hair as he went down the steps.

He returned with a stack of newspapers that he presented to Nell with a flourish.

"Oh, Lewis, thank you. I sure enjoy reading these although this news about the war is frightening. I worry about my brothers and your brothers, too. They're just at the right age to be feeling the long arm of Uncle Sam."

"Yes, ever since Congress passed that Conscription Act in '17, we've been losing a lot of boys to the war. I don't hardly know a family that doesn't have somebody in the military. So far, none of our cowboys have been called up for service."

"I was thinking about that on the way home," Red added. "We should hire some older men for the camps and take the younger cowboys up to the mountains. I want to gather those wild horses. If I can do it, I'd like to look into the remount business."

Chapter Twenty-nine

Getting a Toe-hold

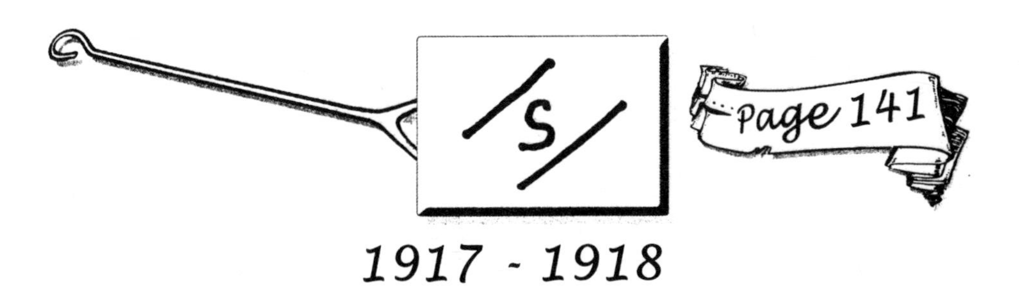

1917 - 1918

Red didn't have to apply for the job of supplying horses for the government Quartermaster Corps. Someone had recommended him as a possible supplier and one of the captains of the Corp in that area showed up at the ranch. Red was appalled at the number of riding, draft and pack horses, and mules that they needed. He had hoped to be able to sell fifty or a hundred head, but now he realized that was a drop in the bucket. They would take all he could ship to them at Fort Reno or Fort Bliss.

Red hastened to set up camp in the Guadalupe Mountains.

Earl Howell, a Texas cousin had agreed to run the camp.

"I'll tell you what, Earl," Red said as they rested after a long, hard day, "we sure have some good hands. They savvy how to capture a wild, range horse and how to green-break it the way the government wants it done."

Earl nodded in agreement.

Red continued. "Earl, I don't want your head to swell, but I'm sure glad you agreed to take care of the wild mustang part of the operation while I scout out more horses. You know a horse inside and out and what to do with them."

Earl sat quietly, as if considering what Red had stated. Finally, he asked Red, "Where do plan to scare up a bunch of well-bred, young horses?"

"I reckon I'll start out by asking all the farmers and ranchers I know. They'll tell me names of other folks and I'll cover as much of

Arizona and Texas as I can."

"Sounds like a good start, Red. I put the word out to all our Texas kinfolk before I left. They'll be ready for you."

"Thanks, Earl. According to what that Captain told me, Uncle Sam may need more than 300,000 head of horses before the war is over. He said the horses were for our allies as well as for our men. That captain said there are hundreds of guys like me with government contracts, all trying to meet the demand."

Red traveled constantly. When he had a good bunch of horses ready, he loaded them on a train bound for the remount station at Fort Reno, Oklahoma.

Red was elated to be on the road again. His pleasure filled him up and it didn't leave much room for feeling guilty about leaving his family alone. He enjoyed the freedom and pleasure of breaking new ground and seeing new country. He didn't miss the monotony of running the ranch.

Sitting in the lobby of a posh hotel, smoking a cigar and sipping a glass of whiskey, Red commented to the gent sitting near him, "I sure do like good liquor, posh hotels and fancy women."

Red swirled the whiskey and contemplated the tip of his cigar. "The fact is, I enjoy food that isn't fried steak, gravy and biscuits."

Red watched the ladies and gentlemen glide through the lobby. The spoke in hushed voices and the women flocked and chattered like bright, little birds.

"I have money in the bank and cattle by the hundreds. Why, I guess you could say I'm a big shot. On day's like this, it's a downright pleasure to be me."

Chapter Thirty

The Sad Trip Home

1918

Red was home for a quick visit on his way to look at more horses when Nell received a telegram. Her mother was dying at the family home in the Chiricahuas. Nell packed quickly and got the boys ready for the trip to Douglas.

Leonard had just celebrated his fifth birthday and Bill was a yearling. Nell had only gone to Arizona to visit her parents once in the years since she and Red had moved to New Mexico.

Nell was thinking about her parents as Red drove her to Carlsbad to catch the train.

"You know, Lewis, sometimes folks get too busy. I should have been a better daughter. Thank goodness Papa is almost as bad as you when it comes to buying every new car they make and heaven knows, he's put them to good use driving out to the middle of nowhere to visit us. They've been out here twice, haven't they Lewis?"

"No, sweetie, I think they've been up here three times, but they didn't stay long that first time because they were worried about the weather. It was late in the fall, remember?"

They drove the rest of the way in silence.

When they arrived in Carlsbad, Red was surprised to see his grandparents, Green and Lucinda Lackey.

"We came up from Texas to see how everybody in New Mexico was doing and we heard about Nell's mother," Grandpa Lackey said. "Nell, you can't manage those two boys and be with your mother in the hospital. We're coming with you."

"Oh, Mr. Lackey, I wouldn't want you and Grandma Lackey to make that long trip. This is your vacation. I can handle it somehow. Besides, with the influenza epidemic…"

"There will be no argument, daughter. We're going. If the Lord sees fit to give us the influenza, then we'll have it no matter where we are, even right here. We'll be on that train when it leaves tomorrow."

The train, crowded with servicemen, wasn't easy to board, but the five of them eventually settled in for the trip. Nell noticed the huge tip Mr. Lackey had given the conductor and realized that was why they had been able to get a compartment together. Nell loved Green and Lucinda, but at first she'd had serious doubts about how much help they'd be. She felt guilty, thinking that she had four people to take care of now, instead of two.

Later, she realized what a blessing it was that they had insisted on coming. She would have not have known how to grease a palm to insure a more comfortable trip for all of them. She sighed with relief, confident now that she had the kind of help she needed to face the upcoming ordeal with dignity and grace.

Each time the train stopped, it proved to be an ordeal. When they left the station in Carlsbad, Grandma Lackey had insisted that each boy wear a medicine bag. Suspended from a string, the small cloth bags contained asafedita.

"Grandma," Leonard complained, "this bag stinks."

"I know son, but the influenza is real bad now. There's asafedita in that bag. It wards off colds and fever. My grandma made me wear it in the winter when I was a girl. She said it would even ward off evil spirits. It must work good, because you can see how old I am."

Leonard still wasn't happy about the acrid-smelling necklace but the mention of evil spirits caught his attention and he imagined fighting off wicked wizards and fire-breathing dragons.

Grandma Lackey interrupted his reveries. "Whenever the train stops to take on new passengers, there will be new germs in the air. I want you boys to put that asafedita bag in your mouth for awhile until the air clears up a bit."

The boys gagged at every stop as they sucked the bags containing the bitter tasting plant extract, but Grandma Lackey was insistent. Nell felt sorry for the boys. She was dubious about the powers of the asafedita, but she, too, sucked the foul wad at all the stops, just as the Lackey's and the boys were doing.

In the tight quarters of the small train compartment, the air reeked with the foul odor of asafedita. If anything could repel germs, Nell thought, surely this could.

Quietly, so as not to alarm the boys, Nell moved them away from the windows and tried to divert their attention at the station stops because there were grey, government-issue caskets piled as high as the train. Each casket held the body of a soldier who hadn't survived the epidemic. The caskets were loaded one-by-one. These dead passengers, young men, were making their final connections on the journey home. The strain showed in the faces of the personnel who loaded and unloaded the caskets.

Nell watched in horrified fascination. She prayed that the asafedita would work to keep them safe, even if her faith didn't.

Red worried about Nell and the boys as news of the Spanish Flu filled the newspapers. A report in a two-week-old copy of the Deming Headlight said that vigilantes in Albuquerque were patrolling the streets to keep out strangers who might be sick. In every newspaper, he saw long lists of the dead. The papers reported stories of the appalling number of deaths in the East. Red recalled a story about Camp Devens outside Boston. The article said that they called the influenza the "blue death" because men turned such a dark color before they died. Some even thought the disease was a return of the "black death."

When the time came for Nell and the boys to return home, Red sent a telegram to his sister, Dovie, who lived in El Paso. The message said: Dovie, tell Nell to stay there. Driving over to pick them up.

Nell had let him know that they were planning to spend the night in El Paso with Dovie before heading to Pecos where they'd change trains for Carlsbad.

The only road across the Guadalupe Mountains was little more than a wagon road. Even in Red's brand-new touring car with a canvas top and isinglass windows, progress was slow. Red longed to take the top off, but the weather was too cold and he knew Nell wouldn't stand for hauling the boys around in an open vehicle this time of year.

Red had been traveling the countryside and he always carried a couple of spare tires. Even with the spares, he was constantly repairing tires. He stopped at a couple of ranches along to way to warm up and have a cup of coffee.

At the end of his grueling trip, Red discovered that his wire had arrived only an hour before he did and Nell and the boys had already boarded the train that morning for Pecos.

Without taking time to sleep, eat, change clothes or hardly say "Howdy" to his sister and family, he headed for Pecos.

He bought two, new spares and hoped he wouldn't have so many flats now that he was on a fairly good road. He could average almost 30-miles-per-hour and he only stopped for a hamburger and a cup of coffee to go while his car was being gassed up and serviced.

Late that night, when he reached Pecos, he saw the train pulling out for Carlsbad.

"Oh damn," he shouted, "nobody will be there to meet them and they'll be stranded in that cold depot."

Red knew that the train was much faster than his automobile. There was no way he could be in Carlsbad when they arrived.

He wired the Eddy Hotel with instructions to have a car from the hotel meet the Lackey/Howell contingent at the depot and take them directly to the hotel where he had reserved rooms for them. The wire also said he'd pick them up the next day.

At the hotel, Nell bathed the boys and they all changed their soiled, travel-worn clothes. Lucinda had dropped off fresh asafetida bags and string replacements, much to the disgust of the boys. When the three of them were ready, they hastened to meet the Lackeys in the dining room.

"Mama, are we almost home?" Leonard asked.

Nell was happy to tell him that they would all soon be at the ranch. Folks who knew Nell stopped by the table to greet her and ask after the family. Nell enjoyed being back in familiar territory where everyone called her "Mrs. Howell."

Red, road weary and exasperated, finally arrived. He took a few hours rest and then loaded his family and grandparents in the car. Green and Lucinda were going to visit their daughter, Elsie, in Lakewood.

As they were getting ready to leave Elsie's, Nell hugged Green and Lucinda several times.

"I never could have made it without you two. I believe you saved our lives – the boys and mine – with the asafedita and all your loving care. Thank you from the bottom of my heart."

Leonard, on hearing Nell's heartfelt declaration, mumbled, "I'd druther had the flu. Let's go home so I can take this damned thing off."

Nell was mortified. She tried to explain that he learned things from the cowboys on the ranch that didn't bear repeating. She said, "I'm fine with the boys learning to rope and ride, but I don't want them to use that kind of language. It isn't fit for good company."

Grandpa Lackey laughed and said, "That's alright, daughter. Just watch him close to make sure he never learns how to throw a Red Howell Fit."

Green and Lucinda at Lakewood
after Nell's Mama died

Nell's mama when she was young
on an ugly old donkey

Chapter Thirty-One

Circulation

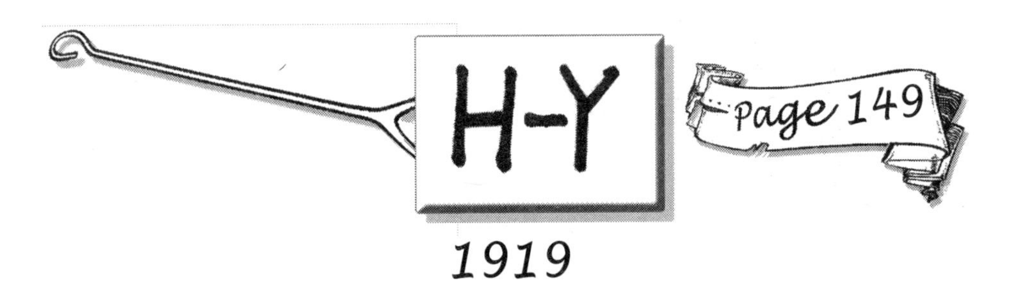

1919

Red was glad to have his family back. He rested up a day or two before he considered trying to find more horses. Between the war and the influenza, traveling had become increasingly difficult. Hardly a family in the area of Lakewood, Artesia and Carlsbad was spared losing a husband, son, brother or lover to the war. If the men survived the war, they were often taken by the influenza at home.

The winter was unusually cold and snowy. Red and the hands rode day after day, pulling cows out of the dirt tanks where they were used to watering. The edges of the tanks were covered with a solid ice. To get a drink, the cows walked in on the ice and fell through where the ice thinned in the middle. A cow, bogged down in the freezing water, didn't survive if a cowboy didn't come by.

"Oh hell, there's another one," Red yelled hoarsely. The cold wind and snow had penetrated through his coat and settled deep in his bones. "I thought we got all these damned cows out of this pasture."

Red and another cowboy threw a loop around the cow's horns, dallied, slowly backed up, dragging the cow toward the shore. Sometimes the tank was deep and the solid ice shelf would catch the weakened cow. The men hollered encouragement and pulled this way and that, hoping to find a weaker spot in the ice, but if the cow couldn't help by trying to scramble out, there wasn't much they could do.

When they did get a cow out, one of the men would tail up the cow to get it on its feet. If the cow could get moving, it might survive.

Every once in a while, a old cow would be on the prod and make a run at the men and horses. Half the time, the cow fell over part way through the run and the men had to go through the whole laborious task again to get her back on her feet. Otherwise the cow would just lay there and die.

"Son-of-a-bitch," one of the hands, Punk Ward, opined, "we should've stayed with the *corrientes*. These Herefords don't have any guts."

Punk had just returned from the war after a tour of duty in France where he'd received a disability discharge.

That night, as the men thawed out and gradually relaxed, all eyes turned to Punk. He was a great storyteller and he was always ready to entertain his audience.

"Pulling that old cow up today gave me occasion to recall I time when I was in Paris, France. I was still in good shape – I hadn't been wounded. I was walking down the street – they called 'em "rooz" over there. I saw a sign that said 'Message Parlor.' I was real pleased because I needed to send word to my ma that I was alright. I figured this was a place where I could I could send a message home. I was especially happy to find this Message Parlor because the sign also said, 'All U.S. soldiers Are Free. They Have Saved Our Nation and We Want to Show Our Gratitude.'"

"I strolled into a real purty room and I thought how nice they were take time to let us ol' exhausted and homesick soldiers wire home for free.

"Now, you won't believe what that little, black-eyed Frenchie girl said to me."

Punk sat back and let his audience consider this. Finally, he leaned forward and continued.

"'Musher, take off your clothes and soak in this tub of mineral water,' is what she said. "'Musher' is what those Frenchie's calls men."

"She showed me the tub and said, 'Here, I'll add some olive oil and you sit in this hot water and relax for 30 minutes."

"By then, it seemed as how that telegram to my folks could wait for a little while. I shucked off my clothes and crawled into that tub full of hot water and Lordy, it felt good. I hadn't had a real bath for a good long time. I sure did relax.

"As I soaked, another girl came into the room and I overheard one say to the other, 'Poor, pitiful man.' I didn't take exception to that. Hell, I've been pitiful all my life and nobody ever treated me as good as they were.

"I was in a stupor when one of the Frenchie girls said, 'Get out and I'll dry you off.' Hadn't nobody dried me off except my mama when I was just a little tad, so I was real interested to find out what this was all about.

"When she finished drying me off, she said, 'Get on that table, soldier boy.'

"I sure didn't know what else to do, being naked as a jay bird. I couldn't see my uniform anywhere. So, I crawled up on that table.

"She started pouring some junk on me and rubbing it in. It smelled just like you do when you come out of a whore house. By now, two more girls had joined in on the rubbin' and they was hittin' spots I didn't even know I had. I wanted to cold-jaw and get out of there before something else happened but, sorry to say, I went to sleep with them rubbin' all over me. When I woke up, I was covered with a blanket and they were all gone.

"I felt better then I ever did when I'd swim with the Joneses in Rocky Arroyo on the Fourth of July. I sort of remember those Frenchies saying something about it doing good for your circulation.

My clothes were there, all cleaned and pressed. I dressed, left the room and started out the door. About that time, I noticed a gal sitting at a tall, skinny little desk near the door.

"'Soldier, it is customary to tip ma sooz before you leave.'"

"I didn't rightly know who 'ma sooz' was. It never would have crossed my mind to call any of those young gals 'ma' anything.

"'Well, ma'am,' I said, 'that sign said it was free and I was more or less taken captive. I've just got $7 to my name and all that rubbin' made me hungry as hell. On top of that, I still have to send a telegram to my ma in New Mexico.'"

"That little Frenchie gal kind of sniffed and said, 'Seven dollars will cover the tip this first time, but you'd better have ten dollars next time.'"

"I never went back," Punk announced gravely as the cowboys hooted with laughter.

One of the cowboys shouted, "Punk, what was the moral of that story? You said it had something to do with that old cow we tailed-up a couple times this afternoon."

"Well," Punk answered when the men quieted down, "you said we had to get the circulation going in those old cows before they could get around good. From my experience, we sure didn't have the right equipment out there to do it."

Me and some of the boys

Chapter Thirty-two

The Angel of the Range

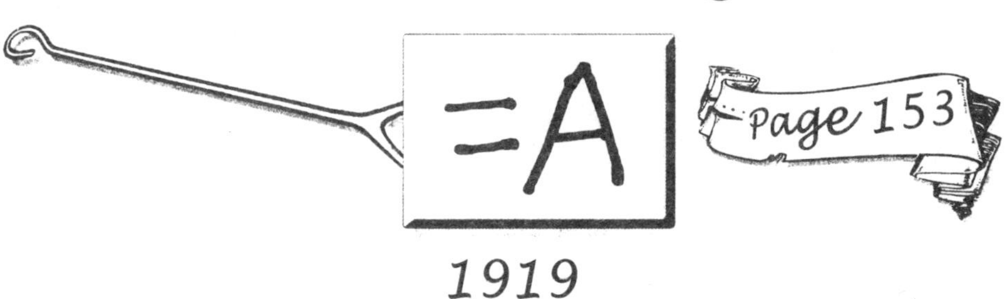

1919

Red had been drafted but the war was over before he was called up. The demand for remount horses dried up almost overnight and Red had time to spend with his family on the ranch. It also gave him more time to rodeo.

Rodeoing was something Red knew a whole lot about and so it was an easy transition into rodeo production. He produced the largest rodeo Carlsbad had ever seen in the summer of 1919. Ropers and riders from all over the West vied for the good prize money he put up and the gate was all velvet, since he used his own rodeo stock.

He also suppled other small rodeos in the Pecos Valley with both rough stock and stock for the roping events. His philosophy was apparent in a phrase he repeated frequently. "Let's celebrate. The War is over."

To Red's delight, his daughter was born in August.

"There surely are plenty of Howell boys to carry on the name," Red told anyone who would listen, "but Howell girls are scarce as hen's teeth."

For her part, Nell was delighted to have a little girl to wear the dainty dresses she had made before the two boys were born. After the births of Leonard and Bill she had carefully packed the dresses away in the cedar chest.

Red had known that Nell would have loved to try the dresses on the boys, but he'd declared, after each boy was born, "This is just not a dress-wearing boy. Save the dress for the girls and put Levis on the boys."

With winter, came a resurgence of the influenza epidemic. All the folks in the rural areas were hoping that they'd witnessed the end of the terrible disease. It seemed especially cruel to Nell, that the ranchers were dealt another blow.

Ranchers didn't have easy access to medical care – medical doctors were few and far between. As had always been the case, it was up to neighbors to help neighbors. An especially wet autumn had made bad roads worse – in many cases the roads were impassable. Ranchers in the Guadalupes often lived at the end of tortuous roads that were crossed and recrossed by streams and canyons. Ranchers, once they finally made it to their destination, recounted stories of spending days and nights in a vehicle waiting for the water to go down enough so a crossing could be made.

Ironically, Red, who was constantly traveling around, managed to stay healthy, while Nell and the three children became dangerously ill.

The Howell Ranch was one of the few spreads that Dr. Culpepper could get to. He came as often as he could. There was little he could do. There was no treatment except aspirin, salt-water gargle and a mustard plaster for congested chests. There was talk of a new product, , being helpful, but Doc Culpepper ballyhooed the idea and said, "The only people that smelly unguent helps are the ones who sell it."

The influenza often progressed into a terrible pneumonia according to the Doc. "Nell, you all have to do everything you can to keep up your strength. If you or the children get pneumonia, there's not much hope that you'll survive. It hits fast and hard. If any of you spit up blood when you cough, let me know right away."

Doc looked exhausted. He had fixed himself a cup of tea and sipped it as he talked. His weariness, Nell thought, is almost painful to witness. Finally, in a soft voice, as if he'd forgotten where he was, he continued. "They can't breathe. They turn blue and struggle until they suffocate. It's as if they drown inside themselves. That horrible pink froth fills their lungs and pours out their noses and mouths."

Doc shook himself out of his revery. "I'm sorry, Nell. I know you're frightened enough without listening to me rant. Sometimes it overwhelms me. I've signed hundreds and hundreds of death certificates and the cause of death is always the same: Pneumonia."

Nell gently touched Doc's hand to let him know she understood.

Red, knowing that Nell and the children were being cared for by Doc Culpepper, made himself useful by going out on horseback to check on the neighbors who were cut off from help. The roads were too boggy for car travel.

It was a nightmarish job to ride up and howdy-the-house.

"Hello? Is anyone in there sick? Hello?" Red shouted.

If he received no answer, he tied his horse and reluctantly went to the door, knocked several times and then entered the house. Even before he turned the doorknob, he often smelled the stench of illness and death. Sometimes he tied his bandana over his nose and mouth before entering. More times than he liked to recall, he entered a house where everyone was dead.

Occasionally, like this time at the Duncan's house, there was someone still alive among the dead. Barely hanging on, cold and hungry – without a fire, food or water – young Homer Duncan needed immediate care.

Red touched his forehead. "Homer, you just hang on there. I'm going out to get some water and then I'll get a fire started in here." Homer, for his part, was too weak to reply, but he moaned softly.

Red wrapped the body of Homer's mother in a quilt and carried the husk of a body out to the barn where it would freeze until it could be buried.

Red became expert at holding a little, sick child in his lap and feeding the youngster water, then milk and finally gruel. Homer certainly wasn't the first child he had nursed back from the edge.

Red fretted in these cases because he had to stay until his patient was either strong enough to ride out with him or was able to survive a few days while he rounded up someone to come out and tend to things. Meanwhile, Red knew that another ranch family probably needed his help and, in spite of Doc Culpepper's visits, he worried about his family.

I feel like one of those jugglers in the circus. I've got three plates up in the air, but in the meantime there are other plates crashing to the ground.

Red was exhausted. He often rode 30 miles one-way and he tried to make his way around two or three circuits to care for neighbors. He never knew what he'd find and he often couldn't return home for several days at a time. When he did get home, he was so tired and discouraged that he wasn't of much use to Nell and the children.

He didn't know much about germs but Red instinctively knew to leave his clothes, boots, even his hat on the back porch so he wouldn't bring the sickness into the house with him.

Nell worried about him. She and the children were finally recovering but it was difficult. She wasn't able to do everything she wanted to do and the children were fitful and cranky. Even bright, clear days seemed dark to Nell.

"I feel like I'm at the bottom of a well," Nell complained to Red on one of his brief visits home. "I can see some light up there, but hard as I try, I just can't seem to climb out."

Red bit back a harsh reply. He noticed that his fuse was a little short lately. "I know sweetie. It sure ain't no bed of roses, is it? I'm just so thankful you are all alive and getting better. One of these days, we'll be looking back on this. Hell, we'll be telling our grandchildren about it."

Ashamed that she'd complained, Nell said, "Lewis, I'm sorry. After what you've been through – all our neighbors, the sick, the dead – you're right, we're so fortunate."

Day after day, Red continued to do everything he could for his neighbors. As the roads dried up, he was able to drive to several of the ranches. If someone died, he'd take the body in the car if the road was clear enough. Sometimes there were more bodies than he could load, so he gathered up several of the healthier men from Lakewood to help him bring in the dead. An undertaker from Carlsbad would be summoned to take care of the deceased.

It might have been possible to have some of the burials at the ranches, but the ground, even though it was muddy on the surface during the day, was frozen deeply and solidly.

Doc Culpepper traveled into Lakewood to look in on his patients there. When he ran into Red, they talked about ways Red might be able to help the people he encountered on his ranch circuit. Doc asked Red about what problems he'd had and what he'd seen and done.

"Well, Red, it sounds like you are doing a good job. You've certainly learned how to apply a mustard plaster and make a strong gargle." Doc chuckled. "I've never heard of your big-snort technique before, but since you are staying healthy, it must work. Keep it up." He patted Red on the back.

Red had a theory that taking a big snort of whiskey as he left each of the ailing families was good medicine. "You see, Doc," he'd explained, "When I leave a place, I force myself to take a long pull off that whiskey flask I carry. I reckon it kills the flu bugs that I might have breathed in and it sure helps me stay a little warmer between stops. Also, I don't have to worry about breathing germs on the folks at the next place I stop."

Doc Culpepper chuckled and watched Red walk away. That man has helped a lot of folks. I've seen those old ranchers get teary-eyed and heard many of them say: Red is an Angel of the Range. I'll surely never forget that man.

My new daughter

Chapter Thirty-three

Ranching Ain't No Walk in the Park

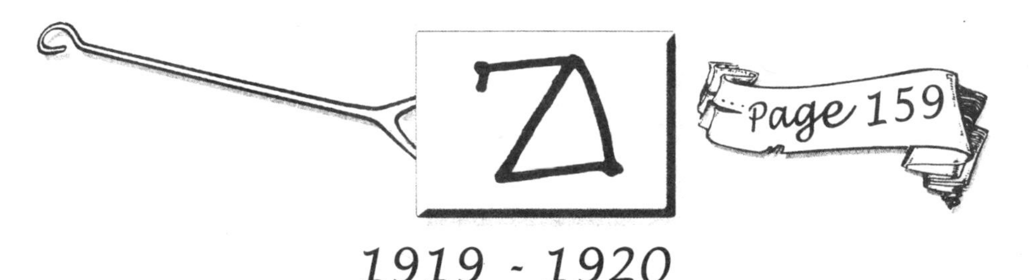

1919 - 1920

Most of Red's cowboys survived the Spanish Flu.

"How're you doing, Slim?" Red asked one of the men who had been working for him.

"Well, I reckon I can't complain. You know, us old cowhands are tough critters. I'd say you're a good example of that, Red. I've heard about what you've been doing. Me and the boys try to stay warm and dry when we can and we doctor ourselves with hot toddies and whatever we have at hand. You know how it is."

"I sure do. Things must be getting better because I've started worrying about the cows. For a long time there, I said to-hell with all those damned cows bogging down out there. Until we got the sick folks taken care of, those cows had to take care of themselves."

"Yeah, Red, now that we are healing up, I guess we'll have to start riding out to the tanks and see what we can do for those dumb son-of-a-bitches."

"When you men feel up to it, I'd like you to take some sacks of cottonseed cake and put it out for the cattle. This has been a rough winter and the cows are sure thin. I've been taking it out with me when I check up on the neighbors. Those damn cows figured out that when they heard the cakes rattle in the sack, it means dinner and they sure come a runnin'. We can use mules to pack it in to those places that are still real boggy."

"Well get on that, Red. I think the boys are starting to feel a little antsy. They'll be glad to get out there and do something useful."

"I heard that the drays from Artesia and Carlsbad are running again. I'll order a ton of hay and some cake. Damn, it sure is nice to be able to get some help."

The poorest cows with calves were brought to the ranch corrals to be fed hay and grain until the spring grass came.

The price of cattle was still higher than a cat's back and well worth the money spent on supplemental feed. To lose a cow was like losing a hundred-dollar-bill. Everyone in the cattle business had struggled through the flu and the harsh weather to get as many animals as they could through the winter.

To his amazement, Red's losses were minimal. The men had struggled valiantly all winter to do what they could. Red's own sacrifices inspired them and they liked working for him.

The men had helped out on other spreads when they could. A lot of ranch owners had died during the epidemic. Red thought it had to do with them staying out on the range trying to save their cattle instead of themselves. They were cold, wet and tired and the pneumonia took them quickly. Now the women were trying to run ranches and raise kids without any help.

It was a sad winter in the Carlsbad area and all over America. Everyone was glad when the days started to get longer, the weather warmed up, and spring offered some hope of a better future.

"Red, Leonard isn't quite six," Nell said. "Is it a good idea for him to be riding with you so much?"

Red gave Leonard a pat of the back and declared, "Why this boy is showing some earmarks of a good hand."

Leonard beamed and Nell could see that he was thrilled to be with the crew and his daddy. Red had been taking the boy with him almost every day this spring.

As she watched, Red tossed their saddles and bedrolls into the Model T, and with Leonard riding shotgun, they headed for one of Red's other ranches.

"Son, there's a herd of wild burros running up in the foothills around Farris Tank on the Four Wells ranch. I sure am unhappy about that. Those damn things keep the cows from getting to the salt licks and the water. They eat the grass that the cows should have and they are a big nuisance."

Leonard thought about this and nodded.

"I am going to have to get rid of them."

Red always carried his 30-30 in his saddle scabbard and he made good use of it whenever he and Leonard saw a burro.

Riding back to the ranch, Red warned Leonard, "Son, don't ever tell a soul about what happened today."

"Why Daddy?"

"Well, Leonard, they'd put your daddy in jail."

Leonard nodded solemnly, thinking how bad it would be if they put his daddy in prison.

As time went by, Red forgot about the burros. He had a lot on his mind. He had some ropings to attend and a couple of big rodeos to produce at Carlsbad.

It was an election year and men were running for County Sheriff, County Supervisor and many other offices. The politicians knew the ranchers were a vital part of their constituency and they often paid personal visits to the ranchers in the hope of winning support.

Red knew them all and wasn't surprised when three of the contenders showed up at the ranch one day just in time for dinner.

Leonard didn't see many outsiders and this bunch flummoxed him. They paid a whole lot of attention to him and seemed vitally interested in what he had to say. Leonard, not one to hang back, let out all the stops. He amused the visiting politicians with stories about ranch life while his mother put the finishing touches on dinner.

Red, observing his son's newfound loquaciousness, decided it was time to quiet things down a bit.

"That's enough son." Red smiled at the politicos and added. "I'll bet you've told them every story you know."

Leonard considered that a minute and then replied, "Nope, Dad, I still haven't told them about you killing all those burros up at Ferris Tank."

The three kids
Bill, Sis and Leonard

Chapter Thirty-four

Most People Call Them Bankers

1920-1925

"Red," Mason Pierce said, "You've always wanted the Whitworth place, haven't you?" The banker stepped out of his office and stopped Red as he left the bank.

"It's the best ranch around here that's close to town. It has plenty of water, some browse, a good house and the best set of corrals in the country."

Red let his mind's eye see the ranch. Abruptly, he said, "I'm skating on thin ice right now. I'm stuck with close to a hundred head of horses the army didn't take when the war ended. I don't have any use for a hundred extra horses and there's no market for them. Cattle prices are down with this drought or I wouldn't have needed that loan today. I'm going to try to hold on to all my cattle until the price comes back up."

"You sure are right about all that, Red," Mason replied. "Things don't look good for you ranchers right now."

"If we just got some rain, there'd be a good market for cows. Everyone has sold down to the bone. There just ain't no feed."

"Red, I wouldn't be in the banking business if I didn't keep up with those things in cattle country. I happen to know you've got a lot of country and you're not hurting as much as other folks," Mason answered.

Red considered this for a moment. "It's a damned shame Mrs. Whitworth has to sell out. Old man Whitworth should've left her better off."

"The bank foreclosed on her yesterday, Red. Old man Whitworth was up to his ears in debts and she just couldn't pay them all off. She's already gone back to Nebraska to be with her folks." Mason rubbed the back of his neck. "I sure hate situations like this."

"Yeah, Mason, I know how you bankers," Red mimicked Mason, "hate situations like this."

Red continued, "I never saw a banker who didn't resemble an old buzzard, just sittin' there waiting for the end to come."

"Watch out, Red," Mason laughed, "You just might need another loan someday."

"See, Mason, you've even got your beady eyes on me. I'll be damned."

"You're in good shape, Red. I'll sell you the paper on the Whitworth place for ten cents on the dollar on what they owed. You can't beat a deal like that. It's no time for the bank to be stuck with a ranch that size. Besides, I'll bet Nell sure would like to be closer to town now that the boys are getting old enough for school."

"Leonard's already in school Mason, doin' good, too. Nell taught him just about everything he needed to know before he started," Red bragged. "They may put him up a grade."

"Maybe he'll make a banker, Red. Wouldn't that tickle you?" Mason guffawed. "Or maybe he'll turn out to be a lawyer."

Red felt unsettled and slightly insulted that Mason found so much hilarity in the idea that his son might attain some professional status.

Mason, recovering from the best laugh he'd had in a while, said, "Let's get back to the subject. There's about thirty-six sections on that Whitworth place. You could run a whole bunch of cattle on that much land. In fact, as you know, it adjoins that Bryant place you bought a few years ago."

"Some of that country ain't worth a cent," Red said, as if thinking aloud. In reality, the horse-trader in him was bad-mouthing the place as part of the negotiation for the lowest, best price. *I'll just see how little I can get that ranch for.*

"I guess you know that land better than anybody," Mason conceded. "You helped her out after her husband died of the Spanish Flu, didn't you?"

"Yeah," Red replied, "I did what I could for her until her brother came down and took over. He sure was a nice fellow. She came from a good family back there. I hate to hear that she lost the place after all the work they all did."

"Red, I'll sell you the papers on the Whitworth place for exactly what we've got in it." Mason named a price that was an unbelievable bargain.

"Yeah, Mason, I'm really beginning to believe you," Red kidded him. "You know damn good and well that you're making something on it or you wouldn't still be in business." Red flapped his arms in a crude imitation of a vulture. "Let me see the papers."

Surprisingly, Mason Pearce opened a worn file on his desk. Red had noticed it when he'd come in that morning. Mason pulled out a sheaf of papers. Sure enough, he had quoted Red the exact amount that Whitworth owed on the ranch.

"I think I smell a rat, Mason. How much were they behind on their taxes?" Red asked. "And, what are you making on it?"

"The interest I'll make off you is where we'll make some profit off a deal that otherwise would end up costing us. I'll tear up the loan I just made you on your signature and lump it all together."

"So, I'll be using the Whitworth place for collateral?"

"The Whitworth ranch plus the Bryant place," Mason countered.

"Hell, Mason, I just got the Bryant place paid off. You want to break me?"

Red wasn't as annoyed as he sounded. He knew the banker was smart. Sure enough, when Mason answered it was exactly as Red had anticipated.

"You'd just throw a lot of cattle on there until the drought is over and then turn it back to us. All it'd cost you is the interest. That's cheap grazing, Red."

"Mason, I wouldn't do a thing like that." Red laughed. "But I would like to have that place. It would sure be handy for shipping. It's so near the railroad and I do need pasture."

"Not only that," Mason added, "Nell would have a good house and lots of water. Why there's even an orchard on that place."

"Nell would be tickled with that. Where she came from, the Chiricahuas over in Arizona, her folks had the prettiest ranch you ever saw. There was a big garden and every kind of fruit tree you could imagine. I don't know, Mason, now that I think about it, Nell would work herself to death and have me farming."

"Hell, Red," Mason chided, "I'll bet you've never held a hoe in your hand."

And that's just half of it my friend." Red paused a moment, making a decision. "Let's get this over with. How soon can I take possession?"

"Anytime you want. We didn't get any cattle with it. There may be a few head still there. We'll sell you the brand. That'll be a little bonus for you."

"Yeah, you know, even with that brush out on Rocky Arroyo, an old cow doesn't have a snow ball's chance in hell to make it with all the long ropers."

When Red told Nell what he'd done, she didn't scold him for mortgaging the Bryant ranch. She hated that place with its alkali water and rattlesnakes. She'd never lived there, but with Red you never knew.

The Whitworth place had a rock house with two large fireplaces and four bedrooms.

"My, my, this place is a dandy." Nell spoke to Leonard as they explored the place while Red, with two-year-old Sis in his arms and four-year-old Bill at his side, poked around the barns and corral. "And, Leonard, doesn't that beat all. An orchard. It looks healthy. Since Mama died, Papa has been at odd ends. He's due back for another visit soon and I'm going to ask him to prune the trees. He'll know exactly what to do to get everything set right."

Leonard, knowing that no answer was expected, nodded his head. His mother was happier than she'd been in a long, long time.

Kinfolk and neighbors pitched in to help and in a few weeks the Howells were settled in their new home.

Meanwhile, Red moved Charlie McDaniels, one of his best hands, into the Adams place and they started switching cattle.

"Damnit, Charlie," Red commented, "My luck sure seems good. There couldn't have been a better time to make a move. Everybody is paying attention to the new place and helping Nell get settled. The folks that aren't helping there are getting the Adams and Bryant places straightened away. Meanwhile Bueford Polk and seven other hands are helping me get a thousand head of bred cows together so we can drive them down to Mexico and pasture them in the Sierra Madre mountains. Those boys are sure anxious for an adventure."

"Yeah," Charlie replied, "I hear that a lot of the ranchers who are droughting out are heading down to Mexico to save their herds."

"Old Bueford and I went down there a few weeks ago." Red chuckled at the recollection. "We had that old Model T flying. We leased a lot of country down there."

"You can bet," Red continued, "that I'm sure glad to have my old friend, Bu, and a good crew going down there with me. I have a whole lot of faith in their honesty and cow-sense."

"If things work out the way I expect they will, when the drought finally breaks in New Mexico, Arizona and Texas, I'll make a killing. There'll be a big demand for mother cows and I'll have a couple of calf crops by then. That should pay all the bills."

"Well, Red," Charlie said, "we're all rooting for you."

Red laughed, "I hear the busiest man on the Pecos these days is the cattle inspector. What with the hundreds of head being loaded on the train day and night at Artesia, Lakewood, and Carlsbad, he's way overworked – even with extra help."

"You know," Charlie said, "I overheard some fellow talking in town. They were saying that no one knew for certain, except for the inspector, how many head of cattle were leaving the country and he was too exhausted to care whose cows they were."

"Yes," Red replied, "I've heard the same thing. They say he just collects the inspection fee, stuffs the money in his saddle bags and heads down the line. I'll bet that fellow has a job straightening all that out at the end of the day."

Red scattered his remaining cattle over a number of pastures and most folks didn't have any idea that he had sent a third of his cattle down south.

One of the fellows taking a rest

Things were going good at this rodeo!

Chapter Thirty-five

Winning Big Money

1920-1925

Summer was in full swing and still no rain had fallen on the arid Southwest. Tanks were getting low and the few springs that were left were going dry. Red continued to shuffle cattle around the pastures eking out the last bit of grass and browse. He assigned several hands to cut yucca stalks, called Spanish Dagger by the crew, from the mother plants and feed them to the cows. These hands called themselves the "Dagger Crew." If they could think of something a cow might eat, they hauled it to the herd. The yucca stalks were particularly good for the cows that were producing milk for young calves. The scrawny little critters thrived as long mom had some yucca to chew on.

Red might have worried non-stop, but the big roping at Flagstaff was coming up. Robinson, Pardee and Gerdner – the three top ropers in the country – had contacted Red. He'd promised to partner up with them in the team tying. He also entered in the calf roping. He knew, even at the ripe old age of 36, that he was better than most cowboys who would enter the contest. His ace-in-the-hole was his horse. Everyone knew that Red rode one of the best roping horses in the country. With a little luck, he might win big money.

When Nell queried Red about the wisdom of leaving the ranch when it hadn't rained and things looked dire, he replied, "What the hell, I'm going anyhow. Charlie can keep an eye on things and if he can't do it, you can."

Red won big money and had the time of his life, made even sweeter in contrast to the bleak situation back home.

"Hot damn, Red," Doc Pardee commented, "this is great. It's just one big party twenty-four hours a day with plenty of girls. I swear, the fun started the minute we unloaded our horses from the train and I reckon it will last until we're pulling out of town."

Red grinned. "You're sure right about that, Doc. Why there's nothin' that suits me as well as a pocket full of money and all those dudes following me around telling me how I'm one of the top ropers in the country."

"And how about those street dances, Doc? You reach out an arm and just like that, it's full of a woman. Remember that Indian strut dance we went to last night?"

Jesse Gerdner joined the conversation. "What I recall is when old Red decided to dance with that Navajo squaw."

"Yeah." Red grinned. "We were pretty well oiled and if my memory serves me, that was a group decision." Red thought about the woman in her ceremonial dress. The scent of campfire and leather filled his nostrils when he'd hugged the young woman up to him.

"They didn't know the two-step or waltz, but they sure were good sports about us blundering in there. I guess we made the most out of that situation," Doc observed, "because I sure had a good time."

When it came time to leave, Red couldn't tell where the hangover quit and the guilt began. He realized that he had given neither Nell and the children nor the ranch a moment's thought since he'd arrived in Flagstaff. To assuage his guilt, he hurried to a department store near the railroad station. He bought a fancy Kodak camera for Nell. The clerk demonstrated how the camera folded out like a little accordion and explained that it took postcard-sized pictures.

While packing his things that morning, he realized he had a Navajo rug. For the life of him, he couldn't remember where he'd latched onto it, but he knew Nell would be well pleased to own a genuine, handwoven Navajo rug. He'd have to make up a story if she ever asked how he'd come into its possession.

Later that summer Red produced a big, successful rodeo in Carlsbad. Ropers and riders from all over the West vied for the good prize money. Although the idea was unspoken, everyone knew the rodeo was the last hurrah for many of the ranchers. They were going under and they wanted to forget the worry and have one, last, carefree fling.

Even Nell went to the rodeo and she took all three children. One-year-old Sis was delighted by the exciting change of scenery.

The boys wandered off on their own, but Nell kept a close eye on the little girl. "Why, Sis, it sure has been a long time since I've been out. And look at me. I'm all duded up. I'm going to dance all night tonight."

That night, Sis held up her arms to Nell.

"Sorry, Sis, you and you brothers and going to stay here Aunt Dovie."

Sis looked puzzled.

"I know it must seem strange to you. I've never left you with anyone before. Don't worry. You're in good hands and I know I won't have to worry about you."

Sis had started playing about halfway through this one-sided conversation. Her mama seemed happy and excited and that was all she needed to know.

Nell was happily surprised to realize that, as Red Howell's wife, she was getting a lot of attention at the dance.

Red, Nell thought, is certainly the man of the hour.

This was their last celebration. Things were going from bad to worse. Banks were closing, ranches were being repossessed and cattle prices continued to plummet. The price of hay and cottonseed cake went higher.

Red had borrowed money on 3,000 head of cattle, but with the 1000 head he'd sent to Mexico, he couldn't produce that many when the bank demanded a count.

The whole ranch was a beehive. The bank wanted to have the count at the Whitworth ranch because it was accessible and had plenty of corrals.

The cowboys were holding the whole herd on a big flat behind the hill west of the ranch corrals where they were doing the count.

Red worked quickly and efficiently, cutting out a couple hundred head of cattle and running them through the gate where the bank's hired-counters were located.

After a batch was counted, the cowboys herded them out and brought in another herd. This process started at sun-up and continued until dusk. Everyone was dog-tired. It had been a hard day. The men had eaten in shifts and Nell lived up to her reputation as an excellent ranch cook. Working without pause, Nell served up a feast to the cowboys who presented themselves at the tables.

The last cow went through the gate and the counters compared their tally sheets. They had counted 3,033 head and agreed that was the correct count. Red sighed in relief and told the cowboys to drive the herd to the Brogdon pasture for the night.

As soon as they finished eating, the cowboys rolled out their bed-rolls. Tomorrow would be another big day putting the cattle back in their respective pastures.

Nell finally got the kitchen straightened out and the table set for breakfast. Wearily, Nell left the kitchen, checked the children for the last time and went into the bedroom. Red, still awake, tossed restlessly in the bed.

"Damn, Nell, I'm as tired and rode down as the horses I used to-day, but I can't sleep. You must be plumb wore out, too, Sweetie. You did a whole lot of cooking for that bunch. I don't know what I'd do without you. He reached for Nell as she slipped into the bed beside him.

"You're right, Lewis, I am tired, but I don't suppose that's news. Any woman who lives on a ranch, has hands to feed, children to raise and a husband with a short fuse she has to be careful not to light, is bound to be tired."

"As tired as I am," she added, "I'm not as tired as I am wor-ried."

Red looked at her and cocked his head.

"Lewis, what I want to know is how in the world did you get that kind of a count on the cattle? You know we don't have nearly that many cows."

Looking downcast, Red was silent for several minutes. Finally, he cleared his throat and began to speak.

"Sweetie, I'm not proud of what I did today, but it was root-hog-or-die. I'd run those cows by the counters and then throw them back in the herd and run them by them again. They'd hang me if they ever found out. Some of the hands might have figured out what I was doing, but I don't think any of them would say a word. They hate bankers and rattlesnakes about the same. Most of our men have lost their ranches to the banks and have had to go to work for wages. They'd never talk.

"I had to do it, Nell, bad as I feel about it. We are just on the verge of losing everything if it doesn't rain soon. I wanted to amount to something so bad, to prove to you that I could. Now, I'm a failure just like your folks knew I was before we got married."

Nell studied the man beside her and realized how worn and old he looked. His hang-dog expression broke her heart. She wanted to reach out and comfort him like a child. Instead, she spoke to him quietly.

"Hush now Lewis and try to sleep. We've got three, healthy kids and each other. With a catch in her voice, she added, "What's money anyhow?"

"It's to spend, Nell, and I've sure as hell done my share."

Sis

Chapter Thirty-six

The Bigger You Are, The Harder You Fall

1920-1925

"Nell, I'm to the end of my rope. National Bank of Carlsbad called in all their loans today and they closed their doors." Nell was cleaning up the dinner dishes and the children were all in bed.

"We don't have everything mortgaged, Lewis. You haven't put any hold on the DX or on Wadcutter have you? And, how about the cattle in Mexico?"

"The cattle in Mexico are the biggest loss of all. This drought we're in has reached all the way down there. It's so remote where I've got the land leased that there was no way in the world to get feed to them like we did here. I told Bueford last week to gather everything and sell them to that big Terassas Ranch as soon as possible to void more losses. I told him just to get what he could for them and for him and the boys to come home. They have worked like dogs down there and did everything possible to save them, but it's just like it is here: No feed, no water, no market. The price of cattle down there has gone to hell just like here. All those thousands of cows that folks sent down there has to be sold. The Mexican market is flooded like ours. I should have acted sooner. I just kept putting it off because I was sure it would rain soon.

"Oh, Lewis, We're right back where we started." Nell sighed.

"I'm going to sell the DXs to Ma and Pa as soon as Pa can move his cattle from Yellow Lake. They'll do good at the DXs and they can pay for it.

"I told Ed Pearce what I was doing. Pa will pay me when he gets here and that way we won't have to give anything from that ranch to any one. I had the other ranches and cattle as collateral.

Nell laughed. "I've always been afraid I'd have to live there and now I might. I wish you could have sold it.

"I'm going to keep Wadcutter. All that's on it are those blasted horses anyhow. Even the bank didn't want it – it's that bad. So, we'll have it for a little income for us. We couldn't make a living there for a family of three kids and two adults anyhow. It doesn't run enough cattle."

"Four kids, Lewis." Nell corrected him.

"Four kids, hell." Red hollered.

"I'm pregnant again Lewis. The baby is due in April, I think."

Well, Nell thought, *judging from that look on his face, it appears like there's a Red Howell fit on the horizon. I'll bet it's going to be a dandy.*

Red slammed his fist down on the table. "What the devil did you do that for, especially now? It looks like you'd think about somebody else for a change."

Nell drew herself up. She could feel anger rising in her like a red-hot poker. "That's enough, Lewis. You're just as much to blame as I am. As old as you are, you should know where they come from."

"Old?" Red shouted. "OLD? What makes me old is you and all these damned kids."

Nell looked at him as if seeing something that repulsed her. "You know you love our kids, Lewis, and you know that not a one of them was planned. I'll get used to this new one and you will too. I certainly didn't want another one, either. There will be five years between this one and Sis. It'll be like raising another family. I'm tired of being tied down, Lewis. We won't even have a home now that you've lost this place that I love so much."

"We've got a year to find something else." Red's anger, like a mountain rainstorm, was intense but brief. Now, his voice sounded hollow. "Ed Pearce said he'd file some kind of bankruptcy paper. We'll have a year to stay here and redeem it.

"It's too bad we're not in Texas because there, the law reads that a man that is driven into bankruptcy can keep his home, his carriage, horses, and tools, so you can still make your living. Here in New Mexico, it's goodbye cows and that means we have to say goodbye to our way of making a living."

"Lewis, I've always thought you'd make a good Texan. They say you can tell a Texan as far as you can see one and when you get up to him, you can't tell him a darned thing." Nell hoped to clear the air a little.

"I wish I'd never left Texas," Red whined. It's been downhill ever since."

"Come on, Lewis, you know you got too big, too fast. What with your smooth-talking, you can con anyone about anything. Easy credit has put a whole lot of people out of business and it sure got us. What are we going to do?"

"First of all," Red's voice strengthened, "it's my responsibility to gather up what cattle are left and turn them over to the bank. They didn't go with the first herd because they're scattered all over the back country. Some of them are so poor that they'll not make it. I want Ed Pearce to either come out here and ride through the roundup or send some banker. I can't afford to put on extra help for their cattle and I want him to see what I've been trying to tell him for two years."

"What about what we owe Joyce-Pruitt and Peoples Mercantile and the feed company? They sure have been good to carry us every year until we ship. I hope we can at least pay them." Nell worried.

"What we get out of those cattle in Mexico will take care of that. I'd mortgage my soul before I beat them out of a dime. Besides, we may want them to carry us again when we get back on our feet. From now on, we'll pay cash or do without." Red said, always hopeful.

"We'll have to pay cash, no one will give us credit now. I can always ask papa to keep us Lewis. He's always got money." Nell said.

"That's hitting below the belt, Nell. I know your papa has always got money" he mimicked, " No wonder he's got money, he never spends any of it. He just sits up there on that ranch on Turkey Creek and the only fun he ever has is when he comes over here to stay a month or so with us and gets all the cat fishing he wants."

"You might be better off, Lewis, if you'd done more cat fishing and not so much tom cattin'," Nell said as she walked off. Very few times in the twelve years of their marriage had Red consulted her about what she thought or wanted, he just went ahead with whatever he wanted to do and told her later.

It was a fifty/sixty partnership. She tried not to resent it but even though she knew this last blow was coming. She was badly hurt because he didn't think to talk some things over with her first.

As late as it was, she grabbed a jacket and went out the back door. Her best grieving place was under the old windmill. She sat on the wooden cross-brace and cried. The slight breeze that always came up in the evening turned the windmill slowly. Even the creaking of the wheel and fan that usually comforted her sounded like a funeral dirge.

She knew she had shared the good times they had before things tightened up and enjoyed having everything she and kids needed, but now the nightmarish dread of living at Wadcutter with alkali water and rattlesnakes made her shiver like a ghost running up her back.

"I'll never do it," she said aloud. "I'll never live at Wadcutter. I'll go home to the Chiricahuas."

She had been so absorbed in her misery that she hadn't heard Red walk up.

He pulled her gently to her feet, put his arms around her and cried.

Nell was stunned. She had never seen a man cry, especially her man. Her heart was breaking too, but it hurt her more to see the big man cry than to have heard the news he had just hit her with.

She snuggled up in his arms and tried to console him, "I really didn't mean I'd go home to papa – I'd never leave you, Lewis, I love you too much. We're in this thing together, even having this new baby took both of us."

This made Red smile a little. Even in the dimness of the fast-approaching night, she could see the tears streaming down his worried, weather-beaten face and she loved him more than anything in the world at that moment.

Chapter Thirty-seven

Cow Chips and Kids

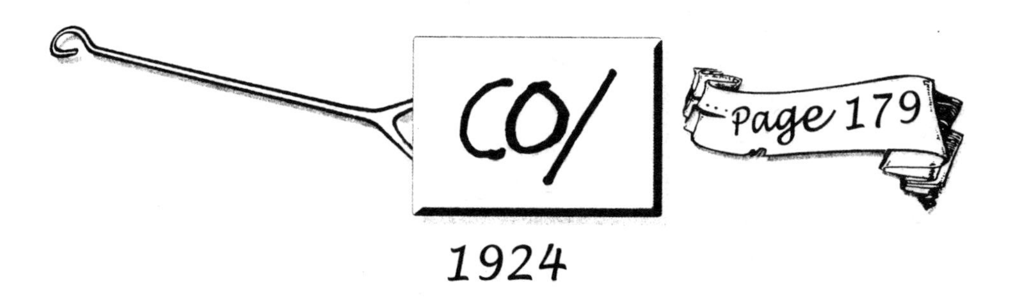

1924

The rains finally came to the parched Southwest, but for many, like Red, they came too late. Most of the ranchers had already gone broke.

Today Red was returning with his saddle horses to the home ranch. Folks still called it the Whitworth place. He had delivered the last hoof to the stock yards at Lakewood and told all his cowboys adiós. Red's cowboys worked for the bank now. They had repossessed everything Red owned except few of his good saddle horses and his roping horses. He'd taken them to the Brogdon pasture and turned them loose.

As he rode toward home, he saw a small figure in the tank-lot where the last of his cows had watered. He reined up his horse and watched his little daughter in her tight Levis and scuffed boots kicking over cow chips.

She didn't look up at Red. She concentrated on what she was doing and didn't see, or chose to ignore, her audience.

Red watched her for a few minutes. Finally, he called to her.

"Hey, Sis, come here."

She hung back, remembering the pain of being of soundly spanked by her daddy. She and Bill had been swinging on the gate. They knew they weren't supposed to do it and they didn't even see Red before he appeared out of nowhere and yanked them off the gate. Sis had never been spanked before and it had scared her. Now, seeing her father looming over her, she wondered what she was guilty of this time.

Reluctantly, dragging her feet, she approached Red and slowly climbed the fence until she was eye-level with him.

"Sis, why in the world were you kicking over all those cow chips?"

"Well, daddy I'm looking for a little sister," she said.

"Under a cow chip?" Red was stymied. "A little sister?" he repeated.

"Uh huh, daddy. Everybody is going on and on about the new baby. I'm tired of it. I figured I should find out where babies come from, so I asked mama."

"And what did your mama tell you, Sis?

Red was glad Sis hadn't asked him that question.

"Mama said she found each of us under a cow chip, so I'm looking for a little sister. I'm not too crazy about that new, little, ugly boy. I asked her why she didn't put him back under that cow chip and look for a better one. I sure don't need any more boys to make fun of me when I play dolls. I've looked and looked, but I haven't found a little sister yet."

Red lifted her off the fence and sat her in front of him in the saddle and rode on to the corral. He let her help him put away his gear and they kept up a running conversation about kids and cow chips.

Smiling for the first time since he'd turned over his last cow to the bank, he could hardly wait to get to the house and tell Nell. He chuckled. Nell had mentioned last night that Sis seemed to wear out her boots faster than the boys did.

On the way to the house, Sis continued to chatter.

"When the boys and I came home from school today, we saw the dust. The cattle are all gone, aren't they?"

"Yeah, Sis, they are."

"We watched the last calf go over the hill. Mama started crying. She was crying real hard, like she was hurt bad. She pulled all of us to her and held us real tight and kept on crying. Grandpa Choate took Clay out of mama's arms. He told us to come into the house and he made us some cocoa. He said mama needed to be alone."

They reached the house and Red saw Nell's red, swollen eyes. He put his arms around her and said, "I'm to damned sorry, Nell. I'll make another stake. It won't always be this way."

Nell nodded mutely, but she knew that it would always be feast or famine with Red Howell. Still hiccuping from all her sobbing, she said, "Lewis, I loved those old cows, every poor, sorry head of them."

Sis piped up. "Good gosh, what am I going to do for cow chips now that we don't have any more cows to make them?"

Chapter Thirty-Eight

Lord Have Mercy, A Goat Ranch?

1925

The cattle were all gone and the dust had settled around the old Whitworth place. Red was seldom home – he was on this deal and that deal, looking for some way to get back afloat.

Rains had finally come to the whole Southwest and the economy was returning to normal. The price of cattle had gone sky-high, but few of the ranchers had the money it would take to restock, even if they had managed to hold onto their ranches through the early twenties.

The kids were all doing well in school. Nell's father was still visiting. He wanted to help Nell by giving her some backup and support.

Nell hated for her papa to see Red come home, half loaded and despondent – if he made it home at all.

One evening, when he arrived home, he stepped out of his three-year-old Model T and didn't reel. He was smoking a big, black cigar – his hallmark for good times.

The kids ran to meet him. Early on, they had learned that if he was smoking a cigar, it meant that he had made a good deal and had brought them treats. Sometimes it was peppermint stick candy, sometimes a box of chocolates for Nell and if it was a really good deal he'd made that day, it was a stalk of bananas, a crate of cherries, peaches or apricots or even a watermelon.

They all shared the treats. Both of the older boys tried to see that Sis got first choice, but Clay, the youngest, was very spoiled and if he didn't get the treat before the others, he would throw a Red Howell fit and Nell would say, "Lord have mercy, it's hereditary."

At the dinner table that night, Red asked, "How would you kids like to go on a camping trip when school's out?"

They were beside themselves. "Oh boy! A camping trip! Where to, Dad? Down on the Pecos fishing? Up to the White Mountains?" They were out of their chairs dancing the Howell tribal two step.

"All of you sit down." Nell spoke sternly. "Daddy is liable to back out if you act like kids."

To the kids, a camping trip meant a gathering with the whole Howell clan. Everybody met at Nogal Lake, the Rio Grande or the Pecos River. The cousins played together, the women cooked and the men fished. A real holiday.

"No kids, this is for all summer." Red told them.

"Now, Lewis, what kind of a wild scheme have you cooked up now?" Nell was becoming a little edgy.

Today I traded that bunch of horses the army didn't take for a ranch up near Queen, on Putman Canyon. I went up yesterday and looked it over. It's a rough son-of-a-gun and it takes a long time to get there. The road is pretty bad after you leave Rocky Arroyo. The house is made of logs and it's probably a hundred years old. You'll love it, Nell." He avoided looking at her. This was not her kind of a house and he knew that she immediately thought about school for the kids. "It's the old DeMoss ranch. They run goats there, so if you don't have cattle that were raised there in that country and are browse eaters, it's too rough for them."

"Goats," Nell gasped, "You'd buy a goat ranch?"

"Well, sweetie, you know that all the auto makers are using mohair now for their upholstery and seats. The market is good and getting better. We'll make a killing."

"Lewis, I refuse to take my children into that kind of an environment. A hundred miles from town. What if one of them got sick or hurt and how about school?"

"It's just for the summer, Nell, they'll have the time of their lives."

Nell cut him short, "Yes, I can see us in a few years introducing Leonard as 'Our son, the goat herder.'"

Red said, "We have to be out of this place by July. I can't see why you think it's beneath us. Hell, we're broke, Nell. We're on bedrock. This will keep us going until something else turns up. I deliver the horses the twentieth of May to them at the Able Ranch at the bottom of Hess Hill. I thought we could camp a couple of nights. You drive the chuck wagon and me and the kids will drive the horses."

"Let's talk about it later, Lewis." Nell interrupted. "But, I'd like to see the place. Tomorrow's Saturday and the kids will be out of school. Let's take a picnic and if I don't like the place, it isn't too late to turn it down."

"Nell, it's too late. I've signed all the papers and transferred the horse brand to them."

Nell interrupted again. "I think, Lewis, since you've messed up so many times, I believe that from now on I should be consulted before you sign our lives away."

"Nell, I'm the one who makes the living, so I'm the one who makes the decisions in this family."

Nell retorted. "The Lord knows you need a keeper then."

Dinner progressed without another word. The children had never heard their mother lay down an ultimatum to their dad. It was scary.

But, they went to see the new ranch the next day. The road up Hess Hill and through the X–Y Ranch to Putman Canyon was an adventure. The car couldn't pull some of the steep hills. Nell drove and Red and Leonard pushed. The other three kids walked.

There were big rocks in the road that held them up frequently and had to be pushed off into the deep canyon on one side of the road or the other. It was a wagon road.

Few cars, even in the 1920s, made the trip up or down Hess Hill.

When they finally arrived at the goat ranch headquarters, Red was appalled as he looked at the place through Nell's eyes.

"Funny," he mumbled." I didn't notice how dilapidated everything is. It stinks like goats."

Red's heart dropped through his boots. Finally, he straightened up and walked over to Nell. In a subdued voice, he asked, "Well?"

"Well, Lewis , we can play like it's a hundred years ago. You can be Abe Lincoln and I'll be Ann Rutledge."

Sis, Bill, Pat and Leonard

Chapter Thirty-nine

Goats in the Guadalupes

1925-1928

Nell surveyed the scene and shook her head. "Sis, everything about this goat ranch sure is unique. Did you ever see goats sleeping in a huge cave at night?

Sis laughed. "Nope, mama, I never saw anything like that. She looked at the corral. It was fenced with page wire to protect the goats from coyotes and mountain lions. Not that page wire would keep out a mountain lion. She glanced toward bunk house where the herders and the old Mexican cook lived. They'd come running in case there was trouble in the corral.

Late that afternoon Nell, Sis and Clay were exploring a canyon not far from the corrals. Suddenly Nell whispered to the children. "Don't look now but a mountain lion is stalking us. Just keep walking and stay close to me."

Nell's mind was working frantically, planning what she would do to save her children if the lion attacked.

As they neared the corrals, the noise of the usual evening activities filled the air. Gratefully, Nell, Sis and Clay, looked back. They saw the lion slinking into the dusk.

Once they had recovered from the fright, Nell found Red.

"Red, an old mountain lion stalked us all the way back to the ranch tonight. He was way too close. We're lucky we got back when we did."

Red had put together a good pack of hounds. He and a couple of the men made short work of treeing the stalker. Red shot the lion out of the tree, skinned him and stretched his hide on the side of the barn to dry.

Later that night, he told Nell, "That mountain lion will make a good rug for the old log cabin."

The years slid by faster than anyone wanted. The summers at the goat ranch were busy and full of excitement for the kids. Red rodeoed all over the West. Nell spent long hours bent over the ancient, wood-burning cook-stove preparing meals for the never-ending stream of friends and kinsfolk who came for a night and stayed for a week.

Occasionally when Red was home, Nell made a request: "Red, barbeque a goat and we'll have a Texas Luau. I'm tired of cooking."

At the end of the day, visitors gathered on the big front porch and swapped yarns. Later, someone wound up the Victrola and the dancing started. Nell, exhausted, was usually asleep by this time.

"Lordy, school can't start too soon," Nell said as she collapsed into a chair one July afternoon. She spoke to Sis, whom Nell had ordered to stay in that afternoon and help out around the house. "I'll be glad to go back to Lakewood. I sure do love that house Papa bought for me. I will be so glad to get away from the god-awful stench of goats. I'll be so happy to be clean from morning until evening with nary a fly in sight."

Sis didn't agree with Nell. She loved the freedom she had at the goat ranch. Nevertheless, she knew better than to voice her opinion. Looking at her mother, she knew that Nell was very nearly at the end of her rope.

Nell and the kids returned to Lakewood at the end of August. "Why, I don't know if I'll every get you wild Indians tamed down." Nell repeated this lament several times as she tried to get the children ready for school.

Sis and Clay fought Nell's attempts to re-civilize them. Although they couldn't articulate why, they resented her efforts. They both sensed that Nell had emotionally abandoned them that summer at the goat camp. Before that summer, she fought tooth and nail to keep them safe, clean and civilized. Once they arrived at the dark, old house surrounded by the smell and sight of so many goats, Nell seemed as if she barely had the energy to move. She didn't smile, she didn't discipline them. In fact, she barely acknowledged them. It was as if they gradually and inexorably become invisible. At first, they vied for her attention, but soon they began to test the limits of her indifference. Most days they were free to roam as far and as long as they wished. Once they realized the extent of their freedom, the children took full advantage of this wonderful opportunity.

In the spring of 1929, Red sold the goat ranch to the Carlsbad Caverns National Park that bordered the ranch on the east and he made a killing.

Before Nell know what was going on, Red had swapped her house in Lakewood for a place in Artesia so he would be closer to the ranch he'd put together the year before.

He was raising registered Herefords and the market was good. With the economy booming, the ranchers were getting rid of their *corrientes* and moving up to Herefords. Red raised some of the best Hereford bulls around, and his stock was in high demand.

Nell had bitterly resented the way Red had cavalierly moved them up into the Guadalupes and onto the goat ranch. Nell's resentment of his high-handed treatment was renewed with this latest move.

Nell found out that Red had sold the goat ranch "as is," so there were no mementos to remind her of her "Guadalupe Exile."

The house Red traded for in Artesia was spacious. It was on the edge of town where the kids could have their horses and Nell could have her chickens, a milk cow and a garden. There were excellent schools within walking distance for the older children. Clay was only four and Nell was glad to have him at home.

Nell's anger abated when she reasoned that Red would stay home more now that they had moved to Artesia. She was wrong.

After a long season in town, when school was out for the summer, Bill and Sis couldn't wait to get out of town. They had never, in their whole lives, spent a summer without going to the ranch — whichever one Red had at the time.

They saddled their horses almost every day and rode out to the "Lone Tree Ranch," as Red's registered Hereford place was known.

It was called Lone Tree because sometime earlier, an optimistic homesteader had planted an apricot tree that had survived the drought of summer and the blizzards of winter. It was a huge tree and it shaded the six foot high steel-rim tank that stayed full to the brim with water pumped from deep under ground by the windmill.

On this visit, Bill and Sis arrived on two, sweaty horses. As usual, when they got out of mom's sight, they spurred their horses into a run to see who could reach the tank first. It was usually a draw. They unsaddled and hobbled their horses so they could graze.

Bill and Sis were too hot to dive right into the cold water, so they sprawled in the shade of the big apricot tree and talked until they were ready to swim.

"Sis," Bill spoke with longing in his voice, "I wonder what's going on out at the goat ranch? Boy, I sure miss that old ranch, don't you?"

"You know I miss it, Bill, I hate this town and those city kids that don't even know which end of a cow gets up first. It's like some foreign country. We don't speak the same language."

"Yeah, Sis, there's never a day that I don't remember something funny that happened out at the goat ranch."

Hey, Bill, it wasn't all funny – you might have thought I was having the time of my life when I stepped on that rattlesnake or when that lion stalked Mom, Clay and me. You were off riding with Dad and missed all the fun. You know, we had a lot of wrecks out there and yours was the worst."

"Yep, I guess I was real lucky to come out of that alive. After that, it sure made me look to see if someone had closed the gate that I had just gone through. I left it open because I was coming right back."

"You sure hit it running with Old Diamond wide open. I will never forget how you looked just lying there, so still, and poor mama trying to run to you from the house, but she'd have to sit down and cough. That whooping cough we brought home from school sure hurt mama, as old as she was."

" Poor mama had to worry about me not waking up. I was knocked out for a day-and-a-half and Dad was off somewhere. She didn't have a car or any way to take me to town. She just had to sit there and hope I wouldn't die."

"Boy, he sure caught it from mama when he got back. You know, Bill, after that she wasn't the same anymore. She just acted like she didn't care about us and let us run wild."

"Sis, remember when they left us at the ranch with Hazel, and Mom rode over to Dog Canyon with Dad to bring back a bunch of cattle he'd bought? We ate down at the bunk house with the cowboys and herders. Boy, it sure was a lot better than Hazel's cooking."

"Yep, that's true. Why, she couldn't even make fudge. Remember that big pan of fudge she made that never got hard and we had to eat it with our spoons?"

Bill laughed. "But Hazel was a good sport about it all. I think she was in love with one of the cowboys and she didn't pay much attention to us kids."

"Mama wasn't any happier when she found out what had happened. Remember, that was when she sprained her ankle so bad. The way she told it, she was leading her horse over some rough spots and slipped in between a couple of rocks and twisted it."

"That's right, Bill. Dad said it swelled up so bad that he had to cut off her boot before they got home."

"And Sis, the next day Dad took her into Carlsbad to get it x-rayed. They thought her ankle was broken."

"All I remember is that they took us to town with them and we stayed a couple of days and went to a movie."

"Yes, I remember that, but what I remember most was having to get haircuts. It's like the pain and the crutches and everything kind of woke mama up and when she realized how shaggy we looked. She was downright embarrassed."

Bill laughed. "You're right. That was funny, Sis. The only time we got haircuts in town those days was when somebody got hurt and we had to go to the doctor. Nowadays mama is always marching me down to the barber shop."

"Hey, Sis, I'll tell you something else that was funny. You know that time you and Leonard were having a burro race from the corral to the house?"

"How could I forget? You jumped out from behind the car and boogered Leonard's burro. I can still see him flying off when the burro turned out from under him. He broke his arm, didn't he?"

"We all caught it for that, Sis. Your burro turned back too, but you didn't fall off. You were bare back and I don't know how you stayed on. An ol' burro is quick!"

"I crossed the finish line and won, but Leonard never paid me. I couldn't gripe too much about it to the folks because we weren't supposed to be racing those burros anyhow."

"Are you ready to dive into the tank and swim a little. Mom will be worried if we're not back by 4:00 like she told us to be. She doesn't like for us to swim in this tank, because it's so hard to get in and out of, but it's better than swimming in that City pool. Don't you think so?"

"Yeah, Bill, I refuse to swim there. I'll bet every kid in there pees in the water."

After a short swim, the caught their horses, saddled them and headed for home.

Out of the blue, Bill asked, "Sis, what do you want to be when you get grown and out of school?"

"Well, I heard a missionary talk at Sunday School a while back and I think I'd like to be a missionary and go to Africa and help all those poor kids."

"Yep, Sis, if they didn't act like Christians, you'd bounce a few rocks off their heads like you do to us boys when we tease you. For a girl, you sure can throw a rock."

"I've practiced enough. What do you want to be Bill?"

"I'm going to be a pilot. When I get out of school, I'm going to learn to fly an airplane. I look up in the sky when I hear one flying over and imagine that's me in there and it's a wonderful feeling to be looking down on everything. Someday everyone will be flying and I want to be ready."

"Maybe you can fly me down to Africa, but I don't know if I'd trust you or not. You'd probably go half-way and decide you were tired of listening to me and drop me out and make me swim the rest of the way. No, I'm not going to fly with you, Bill. I get scared just thinking about it."

The kids, who had initially been so glad to get out of school for the summer, now decided they would be glad to be back in school and have something interesting to do.

When they were not on their horses, they spent time in the city library. Leonard would be a senior and there was a lot of required reading. He got a jump-start on it during the summer in his spare time.

Bill read everything they had in the library on aviation. Artesia was a boom town. New oilfields were opening every day. Science and technical information was changing rapidly, so there was always new material on the shelves.

Sis, not anxious to read anything that might hint of mind improvement, caught up on books written for girls. Even though it was Red's habit to bring home books from each trip, they were all for the Nell or the boys. Now, Sis could lose herself in library books like *The Corner House Girls or Little Women.*

For her part, Nell was relieved to have the kids out of the house when school started. Now she could have time to worry about Red. He was gone more than usual to heavens-knows-where. He was drinking and was cross with the children. Red wasn't cut out for leisure. It was more than he could handle. He had to be building an empire to be able to stay out of trouble.

Chapter Forty

Nell Has Her Dream

1929

The Wall Street Crash of 1929 changed the lives of most Americans and later the whole world. When the bank went belly-up where Red had deposited the proceeds from the sale of goat ranch, he was flat broke again. All he had left was the little Lonetree Ranch and Nell's house in Artesia.

He didn't know where to turn. It seemed he'd always had an ace up his sleeve until now. Daily, the newspapers headlined the number of men who had killed themselves when their money was gone. It was a ripple effect. It wasn't unusual for a rancher, who had survived the Agricultural Recession of the early Twenties, to decide that he couldn't stand this new pressure and put himself out of his misery.

One day Red came into the house sober with treats for everyone.

"Nell, he said, "you've always pined for a mountain ranch like the one where you were raised on Turkey Creek."

"What's all this about Lewis? Have you found another goat ranch in a rougher country than the Guadalupes?"

"No, sweetie." He hadn't called her "sweetie" in a long time. "It's in the Sacramento Mountains near a little town called Weed. Want to run up there and see it?"

Nell couldn't believe it was actually Red who was speaking – asking her to see a deal before he made it.

"Whatever you say, Lewis. I'd sure like to get out of this town. The kids are so unhappy here. All they did last summer was ride out to the Lonetree, run races on their horses and swim in that tank. They don't like these town kids. They feel like they are in jail. And so do I," Nell added.

"Fix a picnic. We'll get 'em out of town for a day anyhow." Red looked better than he had in months.

Three hours later they arrived at the headquarters of the Prude Ranch located near Weed on the Agua Chiquita Creek. It was a good ranch house but not as nice as their house Artesia. There were four bedrooms. Red explained there was no water in the house until the creek ran to fill the storage tank.

"Artesia was the first time I had city water, but it's worth giving it up if we can move out of town," Nell commented.

"We can put the boys in that room that runs the length of the house," Red added. "The cowboys can stay there too. Sis and Clay can each have a room and we can use their rooms for company."

There were good barns and corrals. Nell was thrilled to see a big apple orchard.

Red pointed east, "Look, Nell, there are a couple acres of farm land watered by the Agua Chiquita. The ranch also includes a permit to run maybe 500 head."

"How far is it to the school," Nell asked.

"A school bus runs right by the door that will take the children to Weed." Red pointed up the canyon.

"The Prudes told me that the school at Weed is consolidated and busses come in from three other places. The average attendance is probably 150 from first grade through twelfth."

Nell was ecstatic. It was like coming home to the Chiricahuas.

The deal closed without any snags. Red traded Nell's house in Artesia plus the Lonetree Ranch to the Prude family for the ranch at Weed. It was a perfect solution for both parties.

The Prudes were getting too old to take care of such a large place and the Howell family got out of town.

Red was the happiest of all. He hated the pavement and the cars. He missed the round-ups, brandings and shippings. In town there were no seasons. Just one long, boring existence. Now, he could spread out again and build another empire. Life was good and he was Ol' Red again.

Chapter Forty-one

Ranching, Drought and Depression

1929-1937

The small town of Weed nestled in Perk Canyon in a clearing among Ponderosa pines. A creek, the Agua Chiquita, ran through the valley and was ditched to fields for ranches that had water rights.

A single, dirt street ran through the town. There was a rundown general store that was seldom fully stocked. Two churches – one Methodist, one Baptist – flanked the street. A bar, The Red Dog Saloon On Bloody Gulch, was sided with rough pine and fronted by a big porch. It was named after a popular movie and, as the only beer joint around, it attracted a quite a local following.

The only place in town that showed any regular activity was the post office. The mail was brought in from Artesia three days a week in The Mail Car, which was the only public transportation in and out of Weed. If you caught the mailman in a good humor, you could ride for free. If he was in a bad mood, the round-trip cost 50¢. Of course you had to spend a night or two in Artesia until the next mail delivery to Weed.

Everyone attended church. By 9:30 on Sunday morning, the wagons, horses and cars started to arrive. By 10:00 AM the children and adults were in the Baptist church or the Methodist church for Sunday School and then in church at 11:00 AM for the regular service.

After church the young folks, who had ridden their best horses to town, had match races up and down Main street. Sis, riding her gelding Dunnie, won on a regular basis. Sometimes she won 25¢, others times the bet was for a candy bar or a Coke.

The school building dominated the town. It was one of the few buildings that was painted. Most of the houses in town were built of rough lumber from a nearby sawmill and left to season in the rain, snow and sun to a brownish-gray.

There was no electricity. For water, the residents depended on cisterns that caught the rain. Water for the house was drawn with a bucket tied to a rope. Kerosene lamps provided the light. The cook stoves all burned wood, which was plentiful. Every house had a fireplace – central heating. The high elevation and cold winters meant that the fireplaces were seldom cold.

If you wanted a bath, you heated the water on the stove and bathed in a number-three zinc wash tub in the kitchen in front of the open cook stove oven. Nell laughingly said she would always know her kids by the butt-bar-brand left on their behinds from backing into the hot, oven door.

Everyone had a one or two-seater outhouse with an outdated Sears Roebuck catalog for wiping.

Red was happy. He was doing what he knew and loved best: Working cattle. Adding to his lease land. Buying more and more cattle.

He still produced rodeos at Artesia and Carlsbad.

Each fall, Red drove the cattle to the railroad at Roswell where he threw in with other ranchers. They shipped their cattle to Kansas City, which was the best market.

One of the ranchers, whose property joined Red's, was Buckskin Jernigan. They worked cattle together and shipped to Kansas City on the same train. Buckskin's two sons, Orville and Alvie, also produced rodeos so they swapped bucking stock with Red. The families socialized.

Red always came home from shipping cattle with a pocketful of money and some new Buckskin Jernigan stories.

Chapter Forty-two

A Light from the Windows

1931

Red's bah-humbug philosophy of Christmas was in sharp contrast to the way Nell and the children felt about the Holidays. They loved everything about Christmas and to them it was indisputably the best time of the year.

In addition to the homemade gifts she lovingly created, Nell saved up enough cash to order a few gifts from the Sears Roebuck Catalog. December was the month when the house smelled of fruitcake, cookies, jam and jelly. The jelly jars sparkled like exotic jewels and Nell carefully decorated them to give to her neighbors and relatives.

Nell put the church and school Christmas plays and programs together for the community. She reviewed the speeches and songs and figured out how to make it all work. Everyone in Weed and the surrounding area loved her.

The last day of school, when the Christmas Holiday began, marked a time of frantic activity. When Nell drove up to Weed in whatever car Red wasn't using, she'd pick up children along her route for play practice.

This year, it started to snow early on the day school let out. By the time the children were dismissed, the snow was axle-deep to the school bus. Getting the children home would be difficult.

Nell had ridden in on the school bus that day for the last practice before the big play on Christmas Eve.

Before she left, she announced, "Children, I want all of you to be here by 4:00 PM on Christmas Eve so you can change into your costumes for the performance."

While Nell coached the students, the other parents had been there on the last day of school decorating the big, fir tree. It was a custom in the little settlement of Weed to have a large, Christmas tree for everyone to share.

If a boy was trying to get up his nerve to court a girl, he'd put a gift on the tree for her.

The Howell family made it home early that evening, but the snow didn't stop. The day after school let out, two-feet of snow covered the level ground and four-foot drifts built up in the corners and against the house.

Nell was worried. There were only two days until Christmas Eve and it kept snowing and snowing. How in the world would she be able to get to Weed? Even if there was a thaw, the muddy dirt roads would still be impassable. One thing she knew — she and her kids would get there somehow.

On the morning of Christmas Eve, Nell asked, "Lewis, would you please drive up the road and try it to see if we can make it tonight for the program?"

"Woman, what are you asking me to do?" He looked as if a Red Howell fit was brewing. "You know darn well that nobody could make it up that road. You're not leaving this house. You'd get our kids stuck in a snow bank and freeze 'em to death. I don't want to hear another word about it."

About noon, the snow hadn't stopped and it was getting deeper by the hour.

"Bill," she instructed her middle son, "get Lloyd to help you fill the wagon with that loose hay in the north barn." Lloyd Sweatt was the only one of Red's cowboys who hadn't gone home for Christmas. He was from Texas and it was too far to go for a week's vacation and he was probably broke anyway.

"Then, hitch up the mules" Nell continued. "I'll be warming bricks and getting out all the quilts I can spare. We're going to Weed."

Bill put on his heavy clothes and headed for the barn to find Lloyd.

Red was taking this all in. It was scary to see how Nell's green eyes seemed to burn with fury when she was angry.

Damn, he thought, *the woman is crazy. Here she has a nice house, a roaring fire, and a big Christmas tree in the corner loaded down with gifts and she's high-tailing it off in a snowstorm to help a bunch of little kids sing "Jingle Bells."*

"Well," he mused, "she'll be back when she sees how cold it is out there."

Nell didn't come back.

Slowly, they made their way through the deep snow. They picked up children and their parents who wanted to see the program. They bucked snow drifts all the way up the Agua Chiquita to Weed. It was slow going.

Other people had done the same thing that Nell had. They hitched up their wagons. Others rode through the drifts on horseback to attend the biggest celebration of the year.

The children's Christmas performance turned out well. The kids all knew their parts. The whole community joined in when Miss Close, the music teacher, played the beloved old carols on the piano.

When the program was over and the socializing was done, Nell, the children and the other passengers left Weed in the wagon, The night was beautiful. While they were in the school house doing the program, the snow had stopped. The moon and stars came out and they looked close and bright. All the way down the Agua Chiquita, Nell's passengers sang, laughed and marveled at the beauty of the night.

It was about midnight when Nell and the children finally arrived home. They were surprised when their house came into sight at the end of the long lane. Every window seemed to have lamp burning in it.

"Oh, thank goodness," Nell said. "Maybe Lewis left a big log in the fireplace and we can get warm."

They unharnessed the mules, fed them in their stalls and headed for the house.

Sure enough, the house was toasty warm. The big kitchen wood stove was radiating heat and there was a roaring fire in the big fireplace as well.

Nell almost fainted. Red had the dining table set with cups and saucers and there was a big pot of cocoa on the stove. He was sitting in front of the fire place but she didn't see him. The beautiful piñon Christmas tree was glowing. Red had lit all of the tiny, wax candles in their clip-on holders. It was the start of the most beautiful Christmas she had ever known. In that moment, her heart was filled with love for Red. Maybe he was finally housebroke.

A bunch of friends and family.

Chapter Forty-three

Changing Things For the Better

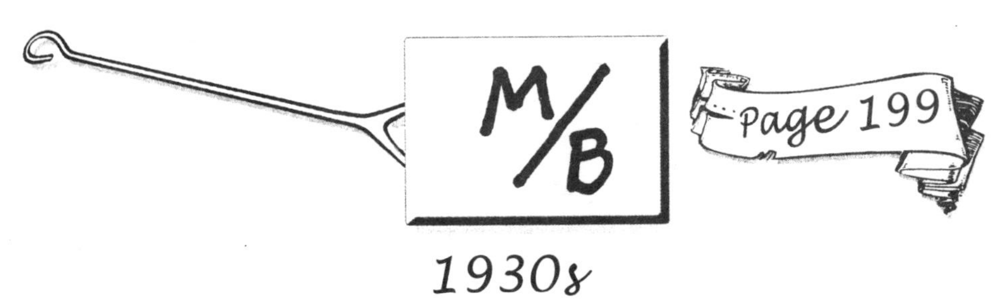

1930s

Nell had organized a PTA at the school. Their primary objective was to get the High School accredited.

With several other parents and teachers, Nell made a trip to Santa Fe to meet with the State School Superintendent, followed by a meeting with the State Legislature to present the petition with the documents that proved that Weed High School was eligible for accreditation.

For the first time in their lives, the children were left with their father. They had a wonderful time. Red didn't nag them to scrub their necks and brush their teeth each morning like their mother did. They ate what their dad cooked. Three times a day they had chicken fried steak, gravy and biscuits and they loved it. Nell left a stew and a pot of frijoles for them. That was gone the first day. She left homemade oatmeal cookies for their lunches but the cookies didn't last as long as a snowball in June.

Red let them drink coffee liberally laced with cream and sugar for breakfast.

In spite of the fun they were having, they all missed their mother. Only Bill and Sis were in school, Clay was too young for school and he rode every day with his dad. Leonard was in his senior year in an Artesia boarding school.

When Bill and Sis got off the bus each day, the house was cold and empty. No hot chocolate, fresh cinnamon rolls or hot soup – the treats Nell always had ready when they arrived home from a long, cold, bus ride.

They were glad when she finally returned. She had only been

gone four days, but it seemed like four months.

It took Nell longer than that to get their table manners back to normal. Sis had been wearing bib overalls to school and she looked like a street urchin. Nell gave her a very stern lecture on how a little girl of eleven who has a closet full of pretty clothes should always dress.

Nell's trip to Santa Fe had Red on edge, wondering if Nell was having too much fun getting away from the ranch and kids, like he always did on his sprees.

In fact, Nell had enjoyed it immensely. Getting away from the ranch gave her a chance to dress up. She had good clothes and she knew how to wear them. It was a pleasure to meet folks and discuss something other than kids, the weather and the price of beef.

She enjoyed seeing Santa Fe, the State Capitol, for the first time. It was even a pleasure to see the countryside between Weed and Santa Fe.

Best of all, the PTA's mission was successful. This meant that Clay, Bill and Sis would be able to stay home and finish high school at Weed.

Chapter Forty-four

Cattle Drive

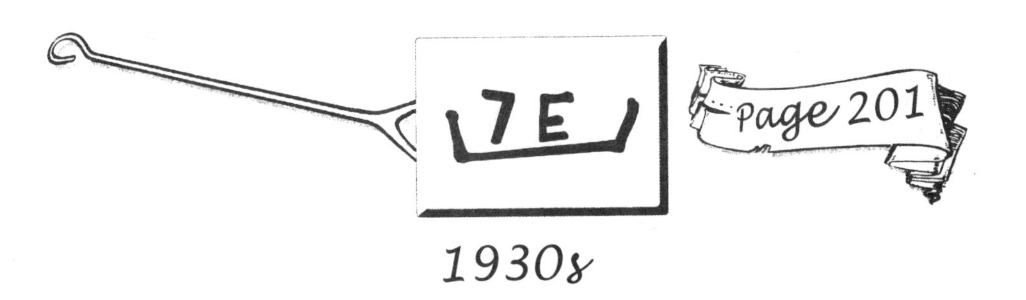

1930s

It was early fall. The Sacramento Mountains of New Mexico were gorgeous. The maple leaves were fiery red and the aspens sparkled with brilliant hues of yellow. The pines, firs, piñons and junipers were the greenest of greens. Cones and berries littered the forest floor. The mountains were saying their farewell to summer .

Earlier that fall, the ranchers who planned to ship on the same train had met at the stockyard office in Roswell. They decided on the shipping date, ordered the number of railroad cattle cars they'd need and contacted several buyers in Kansas City to let them know when the cattle would arrive.

Now, it was shipping time. Red and his cowboys had rounded-up all the pastures, cut out the cattle to be driven to the railroad in Roswell and moved them to the shipping pasture. The drought in the the West had not yet hit Weed and cattle from that part of the country were in good shape and in great demand.

Red and the other ranchers were catching up on chores at home. They would be gone for three or more weeks. It took careful planning to coordinate everything.

The week of the delivery date in Roswell coincided with the annual teachers' convention when there would be no school. Red ordered Nell to drive the chuck wagon, a Chevy pickup. The kids rode drag.

The kids looked forward to this cattle drive as a holiday. They got to go to town and nine times out of ten, it was during the Southern New Mexico State Fair.

Bill and Sis got a lot of heeling practice driving drags. They looked forward to the times when Red rode back to where they and a couple of the cowboys were pushing the cattle to keep up with the herd.

Red looked around and then he'd say, "All right you boys, get down your ropes."

These were magical words for Bill and Sis. On the drive, you didn't do anything without Red's say-so. Now, they'd heel a cow or calf, let it walk the rope off — make another loop and heel another one. This became a betting game for them at a nickle a catch, which the winner could spend on a ride on the Ferris Wheel at the carnival when they got the cattle to the shipping yards in Roswell.

Once in Roswell, the kids went to the hotel where they were staying, got cleaned up and went to the fair grounds with Red and Nell.

They feasted on hot dogs, cokes and cotton candy — things ranch kids seldom had.

Later that night, Nell studied Sis. "You ate to much junk, didn't you?"

Sis, looking green around the gills, denied it.

Back at the hotel, completely exhausted, Sis, half sick from all the junk food, whispered to Bill, "Boy, that was fun, wasn't it? I'm about the happiest kid on the Pecos." Bill grinned and nodded. They both knew it wouldn't happen again for another year.

Red went to Kansas City with the cattle. Nell and the kids headed back to Weed in the pickup and the cowboys drove the saddle horses back to the ranch when Red was through loading cattle on the box cars.

The ranchers going to Kansas City bunked together in the Pullman car that accompanied the freight train for that purpose.

By law, the cattle had to be unloaded every other day to be fed and watered, then reloaded. At one of the stops while the cattle were busy eating and drinking, Red and Buckskin walked to a little greasy spoon café near the railroad to have a cup of coffee.

Buckskin politely introduced himself and Red to the waitress and ordered coffee. When she brought the coffee in was cold.

"Lady," Buckskin told her, "This coffee is stone-cold. Would you take it back and warm it up for me."

She took it back and returned with a fresh cup. It still didn't suit Buckskin and very nicely he again asked her to please warm his coffee.

He said, "Lady, this coffee is warm, but is sure isn't hot. I ordered hot coffee."

Without a comment, the tired waitress picked up the coffee and returned to the kitchen. She put the cup and saucer in the hot oven while she quickly brought the coffee to a rolling boil. She retrieved the red-hot cup and saucer from the oven with a pot holder, quickly refilled the cup with boiling coffee and returned to the table where she delicately placed the cup in front of Buckskin.

"There you go, cowboy. I hope this is hot enough for you."

Buckskin reached for the cup as she walked away. He quickly pulled his hand back as he burned his fingers on the handle.

"Red," he complained, "I can't drink this coffee. It's too hot."

"Saucer and blow it, Buck."

"Hell no, that train is ready to pull out." He called to the waitress.

"Lady, we're going to Kansas City with this load of cattle. We'll be back by here in a week or two. Just save that damned coffee. By the time I get back, it might be cool enough to drink."

At the next stop, they ordered steaks. Again, Buckskin introduced himself and Red to the little waitress and told her where they were from and where they were going and why. This tickled Red.

Old Buckskin is sure a sight.

"How do you like your steak, Mr. Jernigan," the girl asked.

"Oh, purdy good. I eat it three times a day at home."

"I mean," she said, "how do you like it cooked?"

"I like my steaks cooked rare. How do you like yours, Red?" He turned to his traveling partner who couldn't answer immediately because he was doubled-over in laughter.

Red straightened up and replied, "Yeah, Buck, I like my steak rare, too."

When the steaks arrived, Buckskin cut into his and forked a bite. He contemplated the cube of nearly raw meat and the blood that dripped from it.

He raised the fork and dripping piece of meat into the air to get the waitress's attention. When she approached, Buckskin proclaimed, "Lady, this steak isn't done."

"Well, Mr. Jernigan," the waitress replied, "You said you wanted it rare and that's exactly what it is."

"Then take it back and rare the hell out of it some more. If I'd wanted it raw, I could have eaten one of my own cows out there in the corral."

The ranchers from the Weed area unloaded their cattle in Kansas City. They'd found a buyer who offered a fair price. When all the business was wrapped up, they got together and took a taxi to a posh hotel downtown.

Each man shaved, bathed and dressed. Resplendent in their best boots and Stetsons, they went out on the town. All of them that is, except for Buckskin Jurnigan.

"You know, Red," Buckskin said, "I need to find the Sears Roebuck store. Ollie gave me a list of stuff she needs and I want to get that done. Besides, I want to say howdy to them folks. They shore are good to send us the stuff we order. Don't know what we'd to without 'em."

Chapter Forty-Five

Putting By

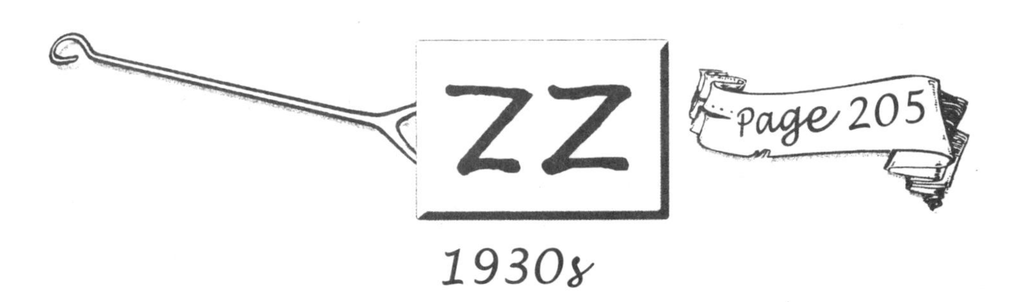

1930s

Even though Red never caught up from the big loss when the banks closed, he was making a little comeback until the drought of the 1930s hit the Southwest. Coupled with the Great Depression things were going downhill fast.

"It's hard to watch the creeks, springs and tanks dry up," Red told Nell, "and to see the cattle lose weight each day. The little calves all look like dogies because the mother cows are not giving enough milk for them."

"Many of the ranchers in the Pecos Valley are in worse shape than I am," Red continued. "My cattle get a little graze from the browse that makes mountain ranches more efficient in a drought than a straight grass ranch."

Red took some of his cowboys down to the DX Ranch that his father still owned and moved a hundred head of his cows up to Weed to try to save them, as they were out of feed and water.

Before the Depression, Red's pa bought a stallion of Beecher breeding from England. He crossed him with the cold-blooded mustang mares he owned and produced a horse that resembled a small thoroughbred. They were in great demand for polo ponies. Red bred a few of his mares to "Beecher" and raised several of good horses, which he broke and trained for polo. Red was able to make a few dollars when he sold the horses to polo players who hadn't lost their shirts.

During the worst part of the Depression, there were many drifting cowboys out of work. They were glad to work for room, board and a little Bull Durham smoking tobacco. Some of them were good cowboys. A few of them weren't worth a plugged nickel.

Food was plentiful. No one went hungry in the ranching communities. Everyone shared, they were more or less self sufficient.

Red kept the smoke house full of meat: sides of beef, a goat or two for Texas Luaus, and fresh and home cured pork. Sometimes there was a side of illegal venison for a change of diet.

The orchard produced apples and pears that would keep in the big bins of the underground cellar until after Christmas.

Nell canned, dried and preserved every kind of fruit and vegetable they raised. From the old-timers, she learned a unique way to store vegetables: dig a pit in the ground. This proved to be a Godsend. The root vegetables and cabbage, broccoli, and cauliflower were buried in a deep pit, below the freeze line and layered with sand. The winters at that elevation were severe, but Nell did exactly as she was taught. She placed vegetables of one kind in a section and placed a little wooden sign at the surface that designated what was buried beneath. This made it easy for the digger to get the vegetables Nell needed for that day.

It was hard to listen to the battery powered radio about soup lines and starving people when the ranchers had so much.

Nell taught the children to pray for "our own hungry kids" and saved the starving children of Asia and Africa until later prayers. It was hard for Clay, Sis and Bill to comprehend. They had never seen a hungry person.

The family seldom went to Alamagordo, Artesia or Carlsbad but when they did, the realized these place had been mercifully spared from dire need. Everyone helped his neighbor by sharing or trading.

When Franklin D. Roosevelt enacted all of the relief programs, the whole Southwest ranching community was shocked. All the old-timers talked about was how the country was becoming socialistic with everyone taking government doles.

Men who had never done an honest day's work leaned on their WPA shovels, drew a government check which they cashed and spent at the bar in Weed. The neighbors continued to take food and clothing to the wives and children.

The CCC camps moved in and took over the small towns with their city boys who were street-smart but didn't know a thing about the roads, fences and tanks they were supposed to build for the ranchers. They caused a lot of trouble in Weed and Mayhill. The nearest law was the County Sheriff in Alamagordo, fifty miles away.

At first, the ranchers and cowboys were not eligible for Social Security – either to pay into a retirement or a disability fund or to make claims. The ranchers would have probably turned it down anyhow because it was a government dole.

In Oklahoma, a prolonged drought caused the Dust Bowl, which effected the whole Southwest. A red, powdery dust from Oklahoma settled in the Sacramento Mountains. When the cowboys rode through the brush or timber, large clouds of dust choked the horses as well as the riders when they were gathering cattle.

Red knew he was going under again. Cattle were being bought up for $18 a head for a grown cow or bull. Those too poor to ship were killed by government men. The rancher was paid $12 for each animal slaughtered.

There was no grass. It was impossible to buy feed for the cattle because the ranchers had exhausted their credit at all the feed stores. Finally, these businesses just closed their doors.

In desperation, Red let his old banker friend at Carlsbad, who also had a sheep ranch on Black River, talk him into taking a thousand head of sheep on halves. Mr. Pearce even delivered them to a pasture Red leased on McDonald Flat. Sheep were bringing more than cattle. A cowhide brought 50¢ but wool was bringing 10¢ - 15¢ a pound and each spring there were also the lambs.

When the ewes started lambing, Red and four of his hands stayed at the sheep camp. Many of the ewes had trouble birthing and had to have help. Lots of the ewe's died, leaving little dogie lambs. It was Sis and Bill's job, when they got home from school, to take turns saddling their horses and riding to the sheep camp which was five miles from home. Each time Sis or Bill returned, it was with a dogie lamb carried in the saddle in front of them. The one whose turn it was to stay home had to milk the old range cows that were kept to feed the orphaned lambs. They filled bottles with warm milk and fed the little dogies morning and night. It was a big chore. All the cowboys were with Red trying to save a few sheep.

In 1936 Red took bankruptcy. All he had left was Sis and Clay's cattle that were not mortgaged, a small farm to which they had to move and some cattle near Weed. Red's rodeo stock and of course his roping horses and several of the horses he was training for polo also remained.

His despondency was Nell's big worry. Nell had seen this before, but never had his despair seemed bottomless like it did now. For days at a time, he wouldn't leave the house.

By this time, seventeen-year-old Bill had gone to Carlsbad to work, so there was only Sis and Clay to help Nell with the livestock. Red still had range on the summit, as they called it, and pastured what cattle he had left there in the summer.

When Red did leave the house, he'd just saddle up and ride to Weed which was not a mile, tie his horse at the bar where the horse would stand until Nell sent Sis up to ride the horse back and tend to him. Meanwhile Red was on a four-day-drunk. The folks in a little town like Weed knew everyone's business. It was not a shock to Nell when the gossip reached her that Red was having an affair with Old Rosie, the town prostitute.

Chapter Forty-six

The Last Rodeo

1936

The fall rodeo in the arena at the ranch where they now lived near Weed drew a lot of good riders and ropers.

The economy was still very bad, but not bad enough for people to miss the biggest celebration of the year, the annual Howell Rodeo. The gate was good. Somehow and someway, the folks raised money for a ticket and the contestants, cash for their entry fees. The broncs bucked, the steers and calves ran and the bulls were almost unridable. It was a number-one show.

The dances and barbeques each night attracted large crowds. Red thought Mr. Clarke, his faithful barbequer did the best job he ever had. The meat, fresh out of the pit and hot from the coals, fell from the bone.

It was like old times. For a little while, Red was back in his element as "Mr. Howell." Seeing him buoyed up and being his old, charming self for a change, almost made Nell forget about his affair with Miss Rosie. Nell planned to address that issue when the dust settled.

The only thing missing at the event was Sis. She left at the end of August to attend the University of Arizona in Tucson. She lived with her aunt Ola, Nell's sister, to save some money. Living in the dormitories with the other students would have been much more expensive.

Vera Middleton, a good friend of Nells, hit the nail on the head when she said, "It sure isn't the same without Sis here. All the cowboys treated her like a queen because she was Red's daughter and they knew if their bull or bronc didn't fire, Sis could talk her dad into giving them a reride."

Everyone missed her at the dances and at the early morning sampling of the barbeque after a night of dancing. At previous events, Mr. Clarke always cut off browned slices of meat and made sandwiches for Sis and her crowd.

Mr. Clarke missed her, too. "Damn, Sis made a party out of everything. This part of the rodeo has gone stone-cold for me. It was purely a pleasure standing around the barbeque pit eating and shooting the breeze until daylight with all the kids." Vera nodded sympathetically.

The rodeo was over: The stock sold or back in place. The excitement was all over.

Red fell back into his lethargy and spent more time in Weed, now not tying his horse at the bar or general store, but blatantly hitching him right in front of his mistress's house for all the world to see.

Nell had enough. One morning at breakfast she said, "Lewis, I'm leaving. I've put up with you for all these years. I can't stand any more. I've been writing to Ola. I've decided to sell everything that I can and move to Tucson. Ola thinks I'll be able to afford a place to live and I'll find some kind of a job."

Red sat there, stone-still, mouth agape. He couldn't believe what he'd just heard. Finally, he caught his breath and whispered hoarsely, "Nell, you don't mean that. You wouldn't leave Ol' Red, now would you, as down and out and with as much trouble as he's had lately?"

Nell, was unmoved by this self-pitying question. His ploy evoked annoyance, not sympathy, from Nell. "You don't seem to have any trouble sleeping around with that old whore, Rosie. I've been shamed enough. If I have to scrub floors in Tucson to make a living for me and my kids, I'd rather do that than have the whole countryside knowing what a lying, cheating son-of-a-…"

Red cut her off before she could say it. "Nell that's enough. I'm against the wall for the first time in my life. I've never been in this kind of a fix. I'm ready to give up."

"You already have," Nell replied, "that's why I'm leaving. You can move in with Miss Rosie and she can listen to you sing the blues. I'm taking the car, the furniture and I've already made a deal with Mr. Boice to buy Sis and Clay's cattle and brands. He can run them here until the bank takes this place which won't be long." Nell's green eyes were blazing.

"You can't do that, Nell, I'm the boss of this outfit. You can't sell those cattle. I'm the only one who can sell them because Sis and Clay are still minors."

Nell looked a him coldly. "You were the boss until you slipped into the gutter. When one of the partners in a marriage can't function properly, the other spouse must take over. It's come to that in our marriage. I have it all arranged. Fisher will be here with his truck next week to take my stuff to Tucson, so you're not needed here anymore. Gather up what you want and get the hell out of here and head on over to Rosie's place.

"It's a good deal for you, Lewis," Nell continued, "you can just sit around and feel sorry for yourself and she can make you a living. I hear she has a great following. "You're just like old man Howell. Irresponsible, not caring anything about your family. It sure as hell isn't worth living with a man like you."

Red, true to form, threw a Red Howell fit and stormed out of the house, stomping and cursing all the way to the barn. He grabbed his saddle and started to throw it on his best horse. Suddenly the full realization of what had just happened hit him. He collapsed on the edge of the water trough and cried.

Red, you sorry son-of-a-buck, you've pushed her too far. When she says something, she means it and she sure meant this. I've gotta stop this somehow. I don't want to live with that fat ol' Rosie the rest of my life. I don't want to give up my wife and kids. I've sure played hell feeling sorry for myself. Leonard and Bill both tried to talk to me and I shut them up. They're mama's boys anyhow. Clay's too young to know what's going on, but I can't keep him. Nell wouldn't let me in the first place and in the second place I don't have anywhere to keep him. I sure don't want to raise him in a whorehouse.

He did finish saddling his horse and rode up to Weed. He tied his horse in front of the general store that belonged to Andrew Boice to whom Nell had sold Sis and Clay's cattle.

"Boice," Red hollered as he entered the store, "I hear you've been doing business with my wife."

"Yes, Red," Boice said, "she told me she needed to sell the kid's cattle to have money to live on, so I bought them and paid her market price. It was a good deal for both of us. She said she was moving to Arizona. It's a done deal Red, there's nothing you can do about it now. The brands are already registered in my name. I've leased where you live from the bank that foreclosed on you, so if you don't mind, Red, I'm busy."

Red doubled his fists. "Come outside, I'll beat you to a pulp, you sneaking bastard. You had no right to deal with Nell on those cattle. I'm the one to deal with. I'm the boss."

Mr. Boice turned and started straightening out cans and jars on the shelves, not paying any attention to Red. Boice reflected on what was happening to the Howells. He liked Red and the whole family. He'd done a lot of business with Red and he'd always been a square shooter in their dealing.

Sadly, things had gone downhill in a real bad way. He knew the whole story. Hell, everybody in town and the whole countryside had witnessed Red's bad behavior. As with Boice, everybody felt sorry for Nell and the kids. They were a good family and there was almost a sense of relief that Nell had taken the bull by the horns.

Boice sighed. The deal with the cattle was above-board and legal. "I'd darned sure do it again to help her out of the terrible situation she's in." Boice directed his comment at the fat, yellow tabby cat curled in a shaft of sunlight by the window.

Red had slammed out the door, rattling the store windows as soon as he realized that Boice wasn't going to rise to his challenge. He mounted his horse and slowly headed back toward home. He wasn't ready to approach Nell. He still had a lot of figuring to do.

Chapter Forty-seven

Tucson

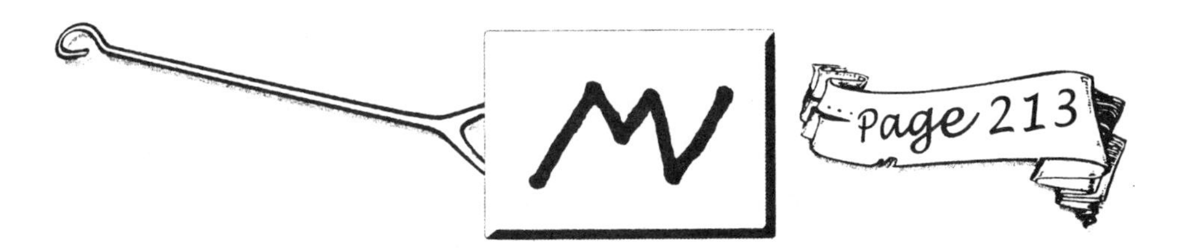

Red and Nell talked half the night. Red had finally come into the house. All day long, he sat with his back against the barn sorting things out in his mind. Looking across the rodeo arena, he saw the low hills where his horse pasture had been. He'd lost it all.

Finally they decided the best thing to do was for both of them to move to Tucson and try to hold the family together a little longer. Clay was eleven-years-old and moving away from everything he knew would tear him apart. Everybody in the family would suffer even more than they already had if Nell left Red now.

Red knew he couldn't let Nell take off by herself with Clay. He had about all of Weed that he wanted right now.

He traded one of his good roping horses for a ton-and-a-half, stake-body truck that was a little long in the tooth but ran good and had new tires. He loaded his last roping horse and the two three-year-old, Beecher colts he was breaking. He threw the saddles up on the stock rack, cinched 'em down and tied the stirrups together with piggin' strings. He loaded the rest of the gear and a camp outfit in cab.

Mr. Fisher loaded the good furniture Nell had collected over the years. Nell watched with sadness as her possessions, collected during twenty-four years of marriage, were either loaded or left behind. The Victrola sat silent. Nell glanced away. She'd decided not to take it. She was leaving many things behind. Vera Middleton had agreed to sell what she could and send Nell the money.

When they arrived at the outskirts of Tucson near the rodeo ground, it was dark. Red didn't know where he could stable his horses.

He knew a few folks in Tucson but it was too late to get in touch with them. He flagged down Fisher's truck and Nell, who driving behind in the old Plymouth sedan, also came to a stop.

"You go on to Ola's," Red ordered. "Fisher and I will unload the horses and stay here with the trucks so nobody will bother things. Come back in the morning with Ola. She'll know where to find a place for these horses and then we'll follow you to the house she rented for us and unload this stuff."

After a few days they were settled in. The house, a cheap little rental on Tenth Street, wasn't what Nell was used to. She was glad she hadn't brought anything else. There wouldn't have been room. Red found a stable, owned by a fellow named Fowler, on Twenty-ninth Street. The locked barn next to the stable provided a safe place for Red to stash his gear. Now it was time for him to look for a job.

His pride was severely wounded. For the first time in twenty-five years he had to ask somebody else for employment. He already hated the town and everyone in it. He loathed being another victim of the Great Depression, the drought and his own inability to cope with being flat on his butt again.

Luckily, he remembered that his roping partner, Ed Echols, was now the Sheriff of Pima County. Ed would know of any ranch jobs because he knew everybody and their dogs in Southern Arizona.

Red walked into the Sheriff's office without being announced. He found Ed rared back in his swivel chair, his boots on the desk, his hat pulled down over his eyes, fast asleep.

"Hey, pard," Red yelled in his ear, "didn't you hear the alarm clock go off? It's daylight. You'd better saddle up."

Ed jumped like he was shot. He dropped his feet to the floor and looked at Red as if seeing a ghost. "You ol' son-of-a-gun. Don't ever do that to me again. I pack a pistol all the time now and I'm always looking for someone to shoot."

He was out of his chair, embracing his friend. It had been a long time since they'd made the Cheyenne rodeo together and won big money. The years had been kind to Ed. He even had a new wife, Benny. Nell had boarded with Benny when she attended high school Douglas.

"Damn, Red," Ed slapped him on the back again, "you sure have good timing. I need a cowboy, a mounted deputy, to patrol El Encanto Estates. You'll like it. We call it the silk stocking section of town."

Later, when the Echols got together with Nell and Red, it was old-home week. Nell was pleased to be able to catch up on all the news.

Chapter Forty-eight

Red Plays His Last Card

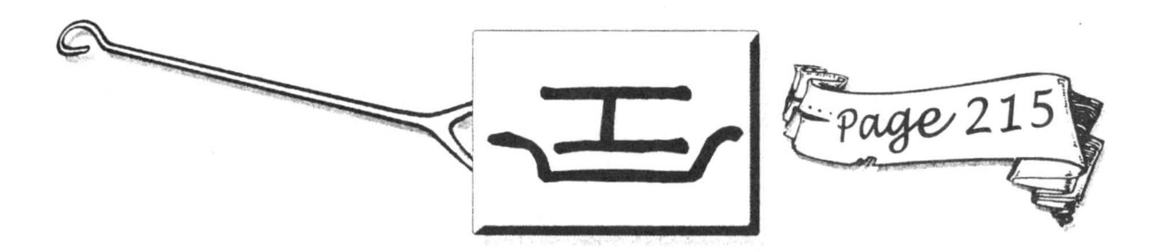

Red was an instant favorite with the city folks.

Riding his bay roping horse, Red started his patrol.

As he rode down the narrow street, he passed a women with a child in each hand. The little boy pulled away and pointed at Red, "Look, mama a real cowboy."

Red pulled his horse around and howdied his new admirers.

It looks like they think cowboys are glamorous, Red decided.

"Please, Mister, can I pet your horse?" Red saw the longing in the child's eyes. He dismounted, tipped his hat to the lady and asked, "Ma'am, would it be okay if I put the little boy in the saddle?"

"Please, mama, please." The boy begged. The young woman smiled at Red, obviously charmed by his gallant request. She nodded her head and Red easily lifted the lad into the saddle.

Red chatted with the young housewife as he led his horse up the street. They had introduced themselves and in the saddle, young Brock was in seventh heaven. As they neared the lad's house, the young girl said, "Mr. Howell, please come to the house for lemonade."

"Yes, her mother agreed, please stop for a moment and have some refreshment. I appreciate your kindness."

From then on, you can just bet Red kept the population of El Encanto entertained. He drank coffee with the young housewives, letting them pet his horse. He regaled them with elaborate tales about all the money the bay had helped him win in ropings all over the country.

Nell was pleased that Red was settling in as well as he was. She knew how he hated the town.

Clay was enrolled in a nearby school. Sis, who had living with her aunt while attending the University of Arizona, moved home and, for ten cents, rode the bus to her classes.

On the weekends when he didn't have patrol duty, Red entered and won a few Sunday ropings. Ed Echols had given up rodeoing since he had been elected Sheriff, but he went to watch Red for old-times-sake and enjoyed the camaraderie of all the other cowboys again. Ed never failed to tell a new audience that he and several other ropers had been invited to England to perform for the Queen. According to Ed's version of things, he had apparently looked good to that royal English lady because she still wrote to him urging him to return.

Nell, Ola and Benny spent hours coffee-klatching. It was like the old days in Douglas when they were all young. They loved to reminisce about the times Benny and her kids from her first marriage to J.J. Benton came to spend the summers with the Choate family on Turkey Creek.

Sometimes Nell almost forgot how poor they were now. It was quite a comedown for all of them, but Nell reasoned that it was better than all the bitterness of the going-ons at Weed. They had a pay check coming in, a roof over their heads, food on the table and Clay and Sis were both home.

On weekends, Sis went out to the Southern Arizona School for Boys where her uncle, Bill Choate, was riding master. Bill also ran a lot of Mexican steers in the desert pastures he leased nearby.

Sis just left her saddle at Bill's. She was glad to get back on a horse and besides, her uncle paid her to gather, brand and whatever else needed to be done. She was beginning to enjoy Arizona a little.

One day she and Uncle Bill were gathering steers to move to another pasture. Bill told her to pick up all the steers in a box canyon and drive them toward the gate into the new pasture. As she rode along looking for fresh tracks, she spied a clear, glass, gallon jug half buried in the sand.

She got off her horse, dug the jug out of the sand.

Bill, seeing Sis on the ground, thought she'd been thrown. The horse she was riding was a little salty and he felt guilty that he'd told her to ride it.

Bill spurred his horse and loped down to where she was kicking around in the sand.

"What the devil are you doing?" he asked.

Sis giggled, held up the jug and unscrewed the cap. She crinkled her nose when she smelled the bootleg whiskey."

"What do you know, Sis, some moonshiner must have stashed that jug during Prohibition."

Uncle Bill swung down from his horse and started kicking around sand to see if there were any more cached bottles. She laughed at her uncle when he found another gallon and said, "Aha!" like he'd discovered a great treasure.

"We'll take these jugs up to the ranch and have a moonshine party tonight. Those professors would love a 1920s party."

Uncle Bill and Aunt Aura loved to give a good party. This one turned out to be quite a bash. Surprisingly, the whiskey was fairly good and it was free. They all tied one on and the next day, half the professors were hung-over in their classes.

When Bill took Sis back to town Sunday night, he poured a quart jar full of the bootleg whiskey for Red.

"Red will enjoy this Prohibition booze. He drank a ton of it. It'll remind him of the old times." Bill said.

It did more than remind Red. He hadn't taken a drink since he left Weed. It tasted good and the more he tasted it, the better it got.

When he went on patrol that night, he was roaring drunk. He rode his horse over the fancy flower beds and watered the bay in the swimming pools. Red sang his old saloon songs half the night and got fired the next morning.

He had sobered up enough after Ed fired him to feel that he couldn't face Nell. He had broken his promise big time and he was down on his butt again.

He drew his pay, loaded his horse in his truck and went back to Weed, leaving Nell and the kids high and dry.

Nell knew this time he wouldn't come back. It was up to her to take care of her family.

Sis quit school and got a job at Courtwright's stable on Speedway. She took out riders on tours of the desert.

Nell got a job as cook at a high falutin' Williams and Steel dude ranch and sanatorium.

Nell and the kids were poor and there was nothing they could do about it but live on the small wages they were making and hope someday something better would happen. Not only did they have to feed themselves, Red had left the two Beecher colts and a stable bill and Nell knew she'd have sell them sooner or later.

Before he got in the jam, Red had entered "Red Sails," one of the colts in a 225-yard horse race. Nell hated to lose the entry money but there was no way she could afford to hire a jockey.

"Mama," Sis volunteered, "I'll ride Red Sails in the race."

"Don't you even think about it young lady. You'll get hurt and then we'll have even more problems than we already have. You may have run a few match races in Weed, but this is a real race with jockeys and I can assure you that none of them are women. You just put the idea out of your head. I forbid it."

Sis disobeyed her mother. It was one of the few times in her life that she had gone against a direct order issued by her mama. On the day of the race, she snuck out of the house, saddled Red Sails and rode to the track.

The first money wasn't large, but some of the men bet on the gal rider because it was very unusual. Sis was relaxed. She was treated courteously but it was evident that nobody took her seriously. She began to enjoy the experience. They lined up and she heard the starter pistol. Red Sails got off to a good start and Sis rode low over his withers. Compared to the races she'd run in Weed, this was quite civilized and she wasn't particularly surprised when she won.

They all split their winnings with Sis and several of the men even asked her to ride for them. She was polite, but she laughed at the notion. In the first place, she towered over the other jockeys and besides that, she knew she was neither capable nor experienced enough to be handling some of the track-spoiled race horses.

Sis had watched her papa get in trouble all his life because he never knew when to go and when to stop. She easily admitted to herself that her win was more luck and determination, than skill. She had no difficulty quitting while she was ahead.

At least now, they'd have enough money to feed the horses until they decided what to do with them.

Red got to Weed the next evening after leaving Tucson. He was almost sober. He parked his truck in Miss Rosie's front driveway, got out, went to the door and knocked.

Instead of Miss Rosie, a rancher friend of Red's opened the door.

"Howdy, Jack." Red stretched out his hand to shake with Jack, who didn't offer to accept it.

"What the hell are you doing back here, Red? I thought you were in Arizona being a deputy Sheriff.

"I needed to come back here, Jack. Where's Rosie?"

"You ain't seeing Rosie. She's through with the likes of you. She wants someone who's not down on their ass like you are. I've still got my ranch and cattle and she likes us big money guys."

About that time, Rosie came out on the porch where the two men were having their disagreement.

Rosie broke in, "You're not wanted here, Red. Get yourself and your horse down the road. You didn't even have the courtesy to tell me you were leaving. I don't ever want to see your sorry…"

Red interrupted. He tipped his hat, made a courtly bow and said, "Lady, the pleasure was all yours." He got in his truck and headed for Carlsbad and kinder folks.

Joker trying to take my hat

Me & Nell We got old

Chapter Forty-nine

Red's Last Ride

1975

Sis spotted her pa as he came up over one of the gentle hills. She and her husband, Sam, had moved from the Deep Creek Ranch to the smaller Houston Ranch near Elgin. This morning, Red had insisted on going out with them to move some cows from the holding pasture to the shipping pasture.

Sam took Sis aside, "Pard, I told you that I don't want Red out there today. We have a lot of work and watching out for him is going to hold us back. You know he misses a lot of cows, so you'll have to pick them up. Those cows know where they're going, so just ride along behind the herd and keep pushing up the cows."

"Driving drags! Why Roanie, I never thought I'd come to this – talking to my horse and ridin' drag. Now I guess if you had a few cows yourself, you could give the powders and ride point. Best they gave me you, old Roanie . When it comes to horses, you are a good one."

"Damn, I can't see too good any more, but I sure can see these white Charolais cows. I wish Sam hadn't got these Brahma bulls to raise some Charbrays. Now isn't that a dumb name. We called all crossbreeds *corrientes* when I had cattle. Guess they've changed things over the last 89 years." Roanie twitched his ears back and forth as if listening to what Red had to say. Red rode easy and relaxed in the saddle and paused to survey the golden, undulating hills that stretched to the horizon.

Red touched his spurs to Roanie and continued his one-sided conversation with the cow horse. "A lot of things have changed and I've seen it all. From riding across Texas on a bronc all by myself when I was just fifteen to seeing a man walk on the moon.

"Hell, I remember the first radio I ever heard. It was the Dempsey-Tunney prize fight. Now all the kids go around with a radio receiver stuck in each ear listening to music that don't even have a tune.

"We thought we'd seen it all when they made those flat records for the Victrola in place of those cylinder things.

"You know Roanie, It's been a good ride. I'm a lucky son-of-a-buck. I been rich and I been poor and I couldn't handle either one. I lived it up when I was rich and blamed everyone but myself when I was poor.

"Guess the best part of my life was when me and Nell bought that little place at Glenwood, just north of Silver City. I sold my last cows in 1955 but I didn't hang up my spurs even then.

"I know it sounds crazy, Roanie, but I had a good time hunting lion and bear with Sis and Sam at Deep Creek. We got in a lot of cow-punchin' too. They didn't seem to think I was too old for that rough country, but they made me ride that damn mule – said he was sure-footed. They forgot to tell me he'd cold-jaw and run under a limb and drag me off. My old elbow still hurts where I landed on it. But it still works. What else do you need?

"Me and my Nell sure got in a lot of fishing there at Glenwood. Trout on Whitewater Creek and catfish in the San Francisco River and a lot of fishing with the kids down on the Sea of Cortez in Mexico.

"I know you mostly like hay, Roanie, but that fishing in Mexico sure gives a fellow some good eatin'. Sis is going to take me down to Tastiota to stay with Leonard awhile as soon as this round-up is over. I can't wait to catch a big grouper.

"Damn, Roanie, these cataracts make me halfway blind but I can still see more than I ought to. Look at that calf." Roanie's attention was already on the calf. Red continued, "He ought to stay with his mammy. If I was a few years younger, I'd rope that son-of-a-gun and drag him back in the herd.

"Well," Red sighed, "somebody will pick him up with their bunch.

Red reined up Roanie and turned in the saddle. He spotted Sis and yelled, "Sis, throw that cow and calf back into the drive."

Sis spotted the pair of fugitives and loped back to pick them up.

Red, knowing that his order would be followed, resumed talking to Roanie. "I sure would like to see my sisters, Dovie and Ruth, and brother Jim once more. We're all getting a lot of rings on our horns.

"If I hadn't gone out to Arizona to see Jim in 1911, I'd never have met ol' Nell. I sure miss her a lot. Let's see, she's been gone five years now. She was sure a stayer. I wonder why she put up with me for 58 years. Shoot, it wasn't really 58 years. I broke out now and then and went on a two or a three-year spree. Bless her heart. She always took me back.

"My sweetie was sure a looker in that red dress when I first saw her at that rodeo dance at Light.

"She raised me some good kids. It about done us all in when we lost Bill in the War. Guess he was a hell of a B-24 pilot from all the stories that was written about him.

"Leonard and Katie have three great kids and Clay and Mary have two. I like 'em all, but I guess my favorite is Rick. Sis and Sam only had one kid, but Rick is a good 'un. I expect he's my favorite because I was around him the most. I fished and hunted with him all the time. Come to think about it, he lived with us more than he lived at home. He couldn't get in and out of that Deep Creek Ranch to catch the school bus if it rained or snowed so he camped at our place.

"He was my buddy, Why Roanie. I remember one time I came by the Blue Front Bar on my way home from fishing on Whitewater Creek and bought a pint. While I was stashing it in the barn, Rick came in. I remember saying to him, "Rick, don't tell your grandma. She thinks I've quit drinking since I got baptized."

"That little kid nodded his head and to let me know he understood. He thought about it for a spell and then he looked at me real serious-like and said, "Grande, when are you going to take me fishing on the Gila?"

"I started to tell him that I had no particular plans to take him fishing and he kind of raised an eyebrow and cocked his head toward the stash. I took his meaning and we went fishing but I called him a blackmailing little bastard. We both had a good laugh over that.

"Speaking of being baptized, Roanie, I got baptized in the San Francisco River. That preacher like to drowned Rick, praying over him while he was holding him under water. I was next, so when he dunked me, I picked up a rock on the bottom of that river and whacked that long-winded rascal on the big toe. Man, he brought me up in a hurry. He was kinda shy of me after that.

"I heard that when Bill Choate was Cattle Inspector in Tucson he was shooting the breeze with a bunch of those ranchers that all knew me, and he happened to mention that old Red Howell got religion and was baptized in the San Francisco River. Bill told those fellows that it ruined the water shed all the way to the Colorado.

" I sure have been blessed with a good memory – thank the Good Lord. There's a lot of things I'd just as soon forget, but thinking back on it is almost as pleasurable as doing it.

"There's the gate, and I'm sure glad to see it. I'm tired.

"Hey Sis, whatcha setting there on that horse like a knot? Get down here and open that gate. Let's pen these cows and go to the house. I need a cold Coors."

Sis & Sam

Me & Rick

Ordering & Contact-Information:

Beth Smith Aycock
1520 W Via De Roma
Green Valley AZ 85614-4624
(520) 625-6080
RedWriter@RagingBrookPress.com

Jorga Riggenbach
Tucson, Arizona
520-250-8393
Jorga@RagingBrookPress.com

In the wild and woolly tradition of the old Southwest, we decided to keep this book as close to the spirit of that era as possible. Beth sketched the brands that start each chapter and Jorga chose a small, family-owned Tucson print shop.

Kevin Johnson, Deirdre DeAndrea, Leo Porras and Kat Knight scrutinized every page that Leo printed on the AB Dick 9850 press. Kat did the layout and created a detailed "map" of how everything should go. Kevin coordinated the whole project and painstakingly cut the stacks of pages as they came off the press. Deirdre was in charge of the massive job of hand-collating the pages. After many weeks of long hours and hard work, the copies of A Red Howell Fit were sent to a local bindery.

This is a truly unique book. We feel certain that Red would have of applauded the idea of keeping everything local and in the hands of the folks who live and work in the community.

Kevin, Deirdre, Kat and Leo.